Qi Jo

Volume 1

A Collection of Stories
to touch the Heart

Michael Tse

Tse Qigong Centre
Altrincham, England

Published by:

Tse Qigong Centre
PO Box 59
Altrincham WA15 8FS
Tel. 0161 929 4485
www.qimagazine.com

First Edition: April 2000
Reprinted: July 2004
Chinese Calligraphy by Michael Tse

ISBN 1-903443-00-8

© 2004 Michael Tse

Dedication

I would like to dedicate this book to all the students who have made this journey an enjoyable one. I hope that we can carry on to keep helping and learning from each other.

Michael Tse

Contents

Foreword

Since 1990, I have been writing many articles for all kinds of publications, including magazines, newspapers, books, a regular column in Combat Magazine (England) and my own magazine, "Qi". There are so many that I even forget what I have written until I read it again.

This book is a collection of some of my stories that have been published over the last ten years. They have influenced many people, particularly my own students. Teaching martial arts and Qigong is my career and I believe that I will teach until I die. There are many kinds of teaching, but for me, teaching without morality is just selling skill. I teach because I love the skill that I have learned and want to share this with others. I teach traditional Chinese skill and teach it in the traditional way. For me, heart is the most important.

This collection of stories covers many ideas and expresses my thoughts on life, skill and shares with you more about Chinese culture and philosophy. Maybe these stories will help guide you on your own Qi Journey.

Michael Tse

Life

In life a person will pass through many difficulties. When they pass through these difficulties, they become strong and mature. For instance if a person is kidnapped and put into a jungle, they must learn how to survive. The same for skill. It must be looked at from all different angles and be tested. If it is good, it will survive.

Michael Tse

Afraid of the Dark

I can remember that when I was little, the thing I was most scared of was the dark. I was frightened to go anywhere on my own in places where there was no light, like dark stairways or alleys. In Hong Kong there are a lot of old, tall buildings that do not have any lifts so you have to walk all the way up the stairs. Because of this I was always afraid to go out at night, even when my parents sent me to buy things. I was even scared when I went camping on the beach with my friends because I always saw the sea at night as very mysterious. I used to think that a monster would come out of the water to catch me.

So of course I was always afraid to be on my own in the dark and ghost stories also frightened me. However, now I am not afraid of these mystical things and this is because I am healthy. Fear is actually caused by weak kidneys. Our kidneys give us the energy to maintain our daily life, so if you have weak kidneys, you will be nervous, lack confidence and be afraid of anything unusual or unknown, for example, strangers, new places, animals, insects, etc. However, if your Qi is strong, you will be calm and confident when you confront these things. Then you will observe them before you react and you will not panic in such circumstances.

So how do you know if you have weak kidneys? You will see some people have a small waist and hips and this is normally a sign of weak and nervous people. As these parts of the body are small, so the kidneys will be small. Some people are born with weak kidneys and these people often find it very hard to achieve a high level of skill in anything. Their mind may not be clear and they may easily forget things and lose concentration. Observing a person's character and also looking at their body shape is one way in which Chinese people observe others and decide whether they are good for a certain position or important job.

If you can develop your kidneys and make them stronger, then your energy will be stronger. Normally, to develop the kidneys we develop the legs and make them stronger. This is because our legs are our foundation, like the roots of a tree. If the root of the tree is strong, then it can withstand high winds and a lot of force. So if your legs are strong, then your kidneys must be strong as well.

If your Qi is strong then you will not easily be scared, especially of the dark or of ghost stories or surprises. Actually, monsters come from your heart not because they exist but because you are afraid and have weak Qi. So even if there are no ghosts or devils, you will create them and be frightened of them. Practise more Qigong and make yourself healthy and stronger and then you too will no longer be afraid of the dark.

A Cat Underwater

Once I watched a programme about Hong Kong born Chinese people living in South Africa. It said that life was quite hard, but some managed to live quite well. These were mainly rich people and as the crime rate was quite high, they had to employ their own security guards, not just one or two, but a whole team who were armed with guns. It was like a small army. They did this because the local police could not respond fast enough.

In one of the interviews, a white South African claimed that many poor black people broke into houses and stole because they were too lazy to work. Personally, I do not know what it is like in South Africa. I do know that black people, like the Chinese, have a very long history and perhaps their history is even longer than the Chinese. In the past, people living in different areas had their own ways and their own culture that had been handed down to them by their ancestors. Wherever they lived, they learned how to survive, no matter if they were in the east or west, north or south.

However, when people from other countries visited some other cultures, they sometimes used their own ways or tools for their own personal gain. For instance, when people of the west first visited China, they took away gun powder, invented guns and used them to conquer many places and kill many people. They set up colonies all over the world. However, instead of following the culture of the countries they had conquered, they established their own routines. The brought over their own lifestyles and forced the native people to follow. Later generations imported cars, aeroplanes, television, radio - even Coca-Cola. How could local people refuse?

Slowly, the native people began to forget their own culture and how they used to live to survive. They began to dress in western clothes, eat western food and even speak western languages. Eventually, they suffered from the same diseases as the westerners. They forgot their history, as if it never existed and lost their entire culture. There was no medicine to cure this. They had to give up their ways to survive, even including which foods were good to eat, which times of the day to rest and work, and the best season to do certain things.

Therefore for this person on television to assume that the black people were lazy is wrong. They are not lazy as they know how best to survive in their own environment. When it is really hot, you should not work too hard, otherwise you will become exhausted. Even in China it is customary to take a break in the middle of the day and have a rest before going back to work. The native people know this, otherwise they would have all died out long ago.

We say in China, "In the summer, a horse does not run too much". Once a western person asked me "Why do you Chinese eat all the internal organs of animals. I have even heard that you eat

9

monkey brains! Is that true?" I replied, "I've never seen anyone eat monkey brains, but I've heard about it. People in different areas eat the food that grows there." Chinese people do not eat internal organs because they are particularly tasty, but because we know they have certain healing properties that help to balance the body, especially the people who live in that area. Maybe there is a deficiency of a particular vitamin or mineral in their diet and so eating something which may seem unusual to us is their way of surviving. So, "like a cat who can never understand why a fish lives in water instead of walking on the ground, a fish can never understand the cat who walks on the ground and does not swim underwater."

More Comfort, More Problem

In today's society people seem to be getting heavier and heavier. We know that being overweight can make you feel slow and not want to do anything except sit and only use the mind. The brain is then the only thing doing any exercise.

Instead of letting the body do more work, we have things that make our lives easier and everything more convenient. All we need to do is press a button. Now we even use remote controls to do our work. Just pick it up, point and press, "doot, doot" and the task is done. We even have lights that will turn on and off by just clapping our hands. We no longer need to walk as much as we did in the past, so our legs become weaker. More driving also forces us into bad posture and so there are more and more people with chronic back problems. Our bodies have become used to inactivity, so the energy we do use is in our brains, for example, watching television, reading a book or playing computer games.

However, these things will make us feel even more tired. Instead of taking more exercise, we tend to eat instead. So the body becomes heavy. But what can we do? When we travel, we tend to use the car or train instead of walking. We sit and rest and take things easy. When we no longer take as much exercise, we become

overweight. Actually, when we become overweight, we create a lot of problems for ourselves as it will affect the heart, circulation, kidneys and cause backache, headaches and even migraines. It can also cause diabetes and other illnesses. When becoming overweight, most people will try to avoid sweet and fancy foods, and eat low-fat foods and drink diet drinks, but this is just a means of staying away from the problem. The best solution is to face the problem.

Our bodies need many different things from the food we eat. We cannot just stay away from some kinds of food, like fats, thinking that this is the solution for curing obesity. This will not solve the problem. On the other hand, overweight people should also not do too fast or too strenuous forms of exercise, as it might not be good for them to handle. If someone is overweight and particularly if they have been for some time, then the body is much weaker. Even standing for five minutes may be difficult. So strong exercise might even cause other problems, such as injury or damage to the joints or muscles that are already weak or put too much strain on the heart or circulatory systems. The best way of dealing with obesity is doing gentle movements like Qigong which can make your body healthy.

Qigong works on all parts of the body, internally and externally, and will rid the body of excess weight. Even with the slow gentle movements you may find yourself sweating as you burn off the fat. However, if you are slim, then you may not sweat because you do not need it. I have seen so many people who join my Qigong classes lose weight within a month and this is without doing any hard exercise, like aerobics or running. Qigong practice is very enjoyable and once you begin, you do not want to stop because you feel so good.

It clears the mind and makes the body healthy. Afterwards, when we do our meditation we calm the mind and let the Qi settle at the Dantien. This gives us more energy and helps us to live longer. In our society, the more advanced technology becomes, the less we need to move our bodies. So while we have all the advantages of improved communications and computers, and less hard work due to convenience appliances, the disadvantage is that we stay away from nature. Everything is indoors. As a result our bodies become weaker. However, if we can balance our bodies by making them more healthy, then with our highly developed minds, we can be both smart and healthy.

Homeless

In the evenings, when I have finished teaching my classes in London, I walk through the streets and usually see homeless people settling down in shop entrances for the night. This way, when they sleep, they are sheltered from the blowing wind and stay much warmer than if they were out on the pavement. This situation seems quite normal today in Britain and everywhere you go, you will see homeless people out on the streets. Many of these are young people, teenagers or in their early twenties. This is very sad to see.

Of course, many people complain to the government that there are not enough jobs to go around. However, when you see these homeless people you cannot help feeling sad. How can a country create so many homeless people? What have they done to deserve it?

However, this is talking politics. I look at things from a Qigong point of view and think of the people who sleep out on the streets and their Qi. Without having to tell you, you can guess their Qi will not be good.

Do you know why we need to sleep on a bed? It is not only for comfort, it is also good for our Qi and blood circulation. On the ground there is a lot of negative Qi as this is where all the waste and the rubbish will lie and the dust and dirt will drop. The floor is usually cooler than the air, and so if you lie on the floor it will take your Qi and you will take the negative Qi which is on the ground. Your body will grow colder and you will become weaker. The earth will treat you as if you were dead. When animals die, their bodies lie on the ground, and the earth breaks them up and absorbs them. So the earth will give you the earth energy to decompose your body. Although your body is still alive, you will get weaker and weaker and become ill the more you are in contact with this earth energy.

When you are ill, your mind will not be so clear and so you cannot think clearly, then everything will seem unlucky. Eventually you cannot even find a job, because your body is too weak. Everything seems to fail and go down and you will feel depressed. That is why once people start sleeping on the streets, it is very hard for them to recover.

Qigong helps us understand that the earth takes negative energy. The good energy is high up in the air, so when you see someone suddenly fall on the ground, you should pick them up and not let them lie on the ground too long. They are already vulnerable and letting them lie there too long will make them weaker still and make it harder for them to recover in the future. Some people might object and say you could cause further injury by moving them. In some cases, this could be true, but in most cases, lying on the ground will cause more serious damage. The earth injury will go into their organs and it can take even longer to recover. Some may never recover their health.

That is why I never recommend people to lie on the ground to take the sun or do meditation. It will take your energy. Have you ever found that on a sunny day, it is very tempting to lie down and feel the sun on your face. However, you also probably know that you begin to feel sleepy the longer that you lie there. This is because the earth is taking your good Qi. Chinese culture is many thousands of years old and Chinese medicine and philosophy too is centuries old. They have learned through observation of nature and people and so although it may not seem scientific, they have watched and recorded the results of many actions and non-actions. Our parents always try to teach us the best way, having learned from their own experiences. In the same way, we can learn much from the ways of China's ancestors.

Witchcraft

Wong Ting Gee's book about witchcraft is very interesting. His book helps us to understand that in the past there were a lot of tricks being played on the public. History makes mention of many immortals. In his book, Wong Ting Gee does not deny that there were many who did have a very high level of skill in Qigong and were genuine. However, there were also many others who were frauds. His book teaches us that we need to open our eyes to look at things clearly, otherwise we would have to treat David Copperfield as a high level Qigong master capable of appearing and disappearing at will.

One story which Wong relates happened in Hawaii. There were some people trying to develop some ancient Hawaiian witchcraft. One man claimed to be a wizard and he would often use a stick in his witchcraft. He would insert his stick into the sand and then cast a spell on it. To do this he had to concentrate all his energy on the stick. He also needed the power of the sea, which was why he practised on the beach by the sea. Sometimes he would sit for a whole day concentrating his energy on the stick and at the same time the sea would give him a lot of energy back.

All the people who lived there knew about this kind of training and no one liked to come near the wizard. Even after the wizard had gone, no one dared to come and take the stick out of the sand. However, there was one young man who did not believe in witchcraft and the tales the people told about it. So one day, while the wizard was not there he went and pulled the stick out of the ground and broke it. However, before the man could leave, the wizard returned and saw what the young man had done. He said to the young man, "You will die in seven days."

The young man went back home and told his family what had happened. Everyone was afraid of the wizard's spell and got very upset. Some even said they knew people who had died when they caused a problem with wizards. The young man then grew more and more afraid. The young man's parents asked many people if they could help solve the problem, but no one could help. However, another wizard said that the young man should go as far away as possible and not stay in Hawaii. The young man listened and bought a ticket and flew to Austria. But it the end, on the seventh day, he died in a bus accident.

Stories like this are quite frightening aren't they? The young man had already suffered from the wizard's curse and his family and friends were also giving him their own curse by making him more and more afraid. He himself created all this negative energy so that by the end of the seventh day, he could be killed quite easily. Perhaps the wizard really did have some power to affect the young man, but if he had just remained calm, not treated it too seriously and built up his own positive energy, then he might have just become ill but would have recovered quite quickly. Maybe, in the end, nothing would have happened to him.

In life, it is important to remain calm, clear your mind, develop the proper energy and train yourself in a natural way. Then other things will not easily affect you. When we practise Qigong, the most important thing is to be healthy and keep your "centre at your centre" and not lose your balance. External things are not important as you cannot take them with you when you die. We should also do the right thing in life. If the young man had not disturbed someone else's property by breaking the stick, then nothing would have happened. So do the right thing.

Sitting up Straight

I remember that when I was young, after school I would come home, spread my homework out over the table and have to finish it before I was allowed to go and play. Many times while I was working, my father would watch me and tell me to sit straight because I would be leaning to one side at the table. Sometimes when I was writing, I would turn the book to one side instead of placing it in front of me as I was writing. My father would criticise me for that and say, "Use the book properly, and don't turn it to the side. And then he would also say, "No bone spirit!".

I remember I did not feel good when he said this and sometimes was even a bit angry. However, today after many years of studying Qigong, I realise my father was teaching me a good lesson. Today almost every child sits improperly. In classrooms you can see children leaning almost like they are lying down to do their lessons. This is because their parents never correct them or because they do not pay any attention to their parents or teachers. But did you know that these bad postures will also damage your Qi? When you practise meditation and Zhan Zhuang (Standing Meditation), you have to keep your back straight to let the Qi sink down to the Dantien.

However, if your back is bent or twisted you will lose Qi and create blockages in your spine and waist and joints.

Often, when people get older the back starts to curve and they walk bent over. This is because their Qi is weak and not strong enough to run through the spine and so their body becomes weak. Eventually, these old people become shorter and seem to shrink. Some cannot even walk without the help of a stick. If a child does not take care of his back as he grows up (for example, always leaning to one side and using only one side of the body), then as he grows, the body will become unbalanced. This will make it hard for him to change when he grows into an adult. When we are sitting or standing, we sometimes want to make ourselves more comfortable. However, sometimes we let go too much and slouch back in a chair or shift all the weight onto one leg. This will accutually make you tired, and if it becomes a habit, it will be difficult to change. Then when you are weaker or older you will have backache and poor circulat-ion. So we should always be aware of our posture. Always sit upright, read in the right position, and stand in a balanced way. We should not become lazy.

Parcicularly for children: do not let them form bad habits when they sit or stand. Many children slouch when they are sitting without realising it. Their parents need to correct them. To be a parent, you have to be responsible for how your children grow and ensure they are healthy and have good Qi.

Qigong

Every day take a few moments to look at the sky. This can release your stress and make you healthy.

Michael Tse

The
Natural Way

For many years, I have been reading Qigong magazines and books. I remember twenty years ago it was very difficult to find good Qigong articles as most of them concentrated on the martial art side. Only just occasionally one or two were connected with Chinese medicine. At that time I was studying the martial art, Wing Chun, with my uncle. He used to tell me about herbalism, bone setting and Chinese medicine, but as a teenager, I was only interested in martial arts, so I did not take it very seriously.

In 1982, China began to open itself more and more to the world. Many new Qigong magazines appeared on the shelves in the shops, and we began to hear of skills that had been hidden for many generations, some had never even been opened to the public before. It was very exciting finding these stories and reading so much information about many different styles of Qigong.

In the beginning, I found all Qigong was reported along with scientific reports - to prove that Qi existed and to show how Qigong cured disease. It was all very encouraging, but as time went by, it seemed Qigong needed all these scientists to prove its worthiness. Personally, I agree all skills and techniques need to prove themselves and see if they can stand the test of time and produce good results and Qigong should also be shown to be effective and safe. However, it does not need to go too far, as in all the scientific studies.

Scientists try to make the world faster, more efficient and increase the level of technology. Qigong on the other hand, has no fast way, only the natural way. Artificial things are not good for Qigong. We need natural things to cultivate our Qi. Too many chemical products, machines and satellites will affect the balance of nature. Plants, animals and humans will also be affected and lose their ability to survive. Eventually, we may all have to live in a controlled environment where everything is fixed and organised. If this should happen, we will lose ourselves, lose nature, lose Qi and lose Dao.

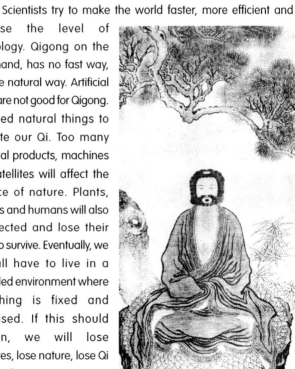

In the past people searched for the way in which to live long and healthy lives.

They lived with nature and learned from it. They needed it to survive and became at one with it. Today we have lots of artificial foods, products and machines. They all make the world look more beautiful, more efficient and more comfortable, but underneath there is another picture. We can lose touch with what is real.

Qigong is a way to bring us back to our true natures and to be in harmony with the universe. We practise Qigong for ourselves and for our health. We practise every day because we want to be healthier and live longer. Of course, no one can avoid death. This we all know. However, we should be able to live our life span to its full term. Today we see many people dying with critical and even incurable diseases. They are like fruit which falls from the tree because it is rotten, not because it is ripe. However, if we act in time, while the fruit is only bruised or before it has been attacked by insects, then we can save the crop. Even if we are already ill, we can still practise Qigong to make ourselves better. Slowly, with every day practice, we can grow stronger.

My teacher told me that when you reach a high level of Qigong, you can even know when it is your time to die. That way you can take care of your business and organise things. There are many other benefits of Qigong, like improved brain power and even healing power. Scientists sometimes miss the point by trying to measure how much and what kind of Qi energy is emitted from the body, looking only at the process and not the end result. I remember reading a book in which a Qigong master was asked, "Does Qi really exist?" She turned to the person and said, "Do it. If it works, it exists." So do not be so caught up in trying to prove whether or not it exists that you forget the purpose of Qigong is to make us healthy, not overthinking to make us ill.

Of course, we cannot understand this level - death. How can we before we get there? It is like a waterfall. Before it falls to the next stage the water flows faster and even its fragrance is different. I hope that everyone who practises Qigong will reach a high level as we do not need to be afraid of death and can die happily. There is no need to prove Qigong with science. The most important thing is that you are healthy and this is enough. We cannot rid ourselves of modern society, but we don't want to spoil things for the next generation.

How to Practise Qigong?

Recently, many people have asked me about the proper way to practise Qigong. They say that when they practise they feel cold or at night they cannot sleep. Some have even said that their kidneys feel weak or they have no energy and still feel pain. Sometimes the reason for this is that the person is practising incorrectly or they have been taught incorrectly by their teacher. Because Qigong is becoming so popular, there is no shortage of teachers, books and videos for people to choose from.

However, not all of these people know Qigong deeply enough. Sometimes they mislead their students, either promising quick or miracle results. Sometimes they will instruct their students incorrectly in a movement, not knowing the principle of the Qigong style which they are teaching. This can even lead to a serious health problem for the student because they have been doing a movement incorrectly and creating the wrong energy in the body.

Once when I was quite young, I bought a Qigong book. I knew Qigong was very good for the body and assumed it was very easy to study. I was keen to feel the flow of my Qi. After reading some of the book, I lay on my bed, relaxed and concentrated on my breathing. Suddenly I heard some sounds. I could not work out where they were coming from and then realised it was from inside me! This scared me, so I stopped meditating. My teacher later told me that because I was trying to focus and concentrate too much on my body, my brain reacted and created the sound. She also said that it was not unusual to hear sounds during meditation and that if I relaxed more then it would not happen again. Maybe the book was good, but at that time how could I know? I was too inexperienced.

Qigong deals with the internal body and Qi. You need a good teacher to guide you. It is not the same as a technical skill such as fixing your washing machine. If you get it wrong, you cannot just stop and start again. If you find a good teacher, then you can tell which books are good and which are not. If you are not able to study with someone, and you can only do so through a book or video, then you should try to find out as much as possible about the person who wrote the book or made the video. Find out what is their skill and experience and what is the lineage or background of the Qigong or skill they are teaching. Has it been around for many years to prove it is safe? Do they have any students whom you can talk to? These questions will help you make a better choice.

One of my students once gave me a video tape of someone calling themselves a Qigong Master who had filmed themselves doing one of the Qigong forms that I teach. They had so many movements wrong and it was obvious that they had not studied properly, maybe just at a seminar in China. Yet here they were trying to make money out of selling this Qigong skill. I know that anyone studying a long

time with this tape would have health problems as many of the postures and movements were incorrect. I know that the person did not really have a bad heart and that they probably only wanted to share this skill with others. However, by going about it in this way, they could easily cause other people to have problems or make their health condition worsen. I feel sad to see this and so I always tell my students to study properly.

At other times, it is not the teacher but the student who creates a problem. This is because they have not followed their teacher's directions. Instead of following what their teacher says, they will try to direct the Qi in their body or visualise too much, closing the eyes when they should be open. Maybe they breathe through the mouth when they have been instructed to breathe through the nose. In Qigong practise, we breathe through the nose. Otherwise the Qi will not sink to the Dantien. These students, instead of cultivating energy, are using their energy. This can in turn cause side effects or what the Chinese call, "Releasing the fire, the devil comes in". Basically the way they practise is not natural. If the method they are using is not natural then there must be something wrong. Some people try to use the mind to direct the Qi to flow along the channels. They want to smooth all their channels and they want to form their "microcosmic orbit" or "Xiao Zhou Tian". However, the harder they try, the more side effects they get!

Qigong is based upon nature and we should follow nature when we practise. This means that the correct way to practise is to take it easy. You should practise your exercises naturally and with a relaxed mind. You do not need to think about how the Qi flows or when your Xiao Zhou Tian will form. When you reach the right level, it will naturally happen. Sometimes, the more we want something, the further away it will go or the result will not last. The best way to practise Qigong is to not think too much, empty your mind and enjoy your practice.

I have seen people, even some of my own students who have been with me for many years, who say they are practising Qigong everyday but still are not healthy. Maybe they still have a back problem or their circulation is still poor or their mind is not settled. This is not because Qigong does not work. Although they practise, they may not practise with the right energy or attitude. Other times it is because they are still using more energy than they gain through their practise.

I remember one lady who was always very busy. She worked as well as going to school to study. In addition to Qigong, she also had many other interests. Every time she came to class I saw that her back problem was not getting any better. She still had difficulty standing for long periods but instead of dropping some of the other things and relaxing more, she felt that she was not receiving enough attention in class and so kept coming later and later to have her lesson. Eventually she even stopped coming to Qigong class altogether.

Another case was someone who had studied with me many years practising Dayan Qigong. Although she loved Qigong, she could not settle her mind enough to concentrate because she did not do enough meditation to balance her practice and other things going on in her life. Although her movements were correct and she knew the acupuncture points, she had missed the principle.

Qigong is about balancing our bodies and minds. I have often said that when we practise, it is like putting money into our savings account at the bank. This is energy which the body can store in order to make us more healthy. However, although she practised, she was using more energy than she had gathered. She was overdrawing on her bank account. So although her health was better than when she first began to study with me, it was still not as good as it should have been. I could still see she had liver and circulation problems. So until she changes her lifestyle or increases her practise to gather more energy than she uses, her Qigong level will not be very high.

Sometimes we see people who do not practise Qigong but who are quite healthy. This is because their lives are balanced. They know when to rest, what and how much food to eat at the right time, when to work and play. My Wing Chun teacher, Grandmaster Ip Chun, is one of these people. His martial arts technique always impresses people. In one seminar he spent over two hours playing Sticking Hands with around thirty different people, all aged between 20 to 30. No one could touch him even though all these young men tried their best to use their speed and strength. He fended them all off easily and he was not even out of breath or tired. At the end, some people thought that this was because he must practise some form of Qigong to keep himself fit and strong in addition to his Wing Chun.

Actually they were wrong! Sifu has never studied any kind of Qigong. He just practises his Wing Chun Sticking Hands and sometimes goes to the mountains and walks for miles and miles. If he is tired, he knows to rest and he says he never eats to be completely full, so he also takes care of his digestion. However, during his training he unconsciously covers the elements of Qigong practice. Whilst practising Sticking Hands with his students, his mind is calm. He does not have to think. By practising the Wing Chun forms, he has taught his body how to relax and so his breathing comes very naturally and co-ordinates with his movements. The Qi develops and moves naturally through his body without him even thinking about it. Actually, he has reached a very high level of Qigong without even thinking about it. This is what Qigong should be: "Heaven and man come together to be one". Then you become part of the universe and so your life and energy will go on and not change a great deal.

What is Qi?

"I don't believe in Qi!"

"It's impossible!"

"I don't believe you can move a person without touching them!"

"It's just psychological!"

When I hear some people say these things, I think to myself "Great! Keep saying that. Don't change until you die!" I often hear this from people who have never heard of Qigong or Qi. However, recently I heard someone say this who practised Taijiquan, a martial art whose very concept is based upon the balance of yin and yang energies (or Qi).

Nowadays, many scientists and western medical doctors are going on to study acupuncture, Qigong, Homeopathy, Feng Shui, etc. because they too want to find out what Qi is as well as more about eastern culture and skill. Through their studies, they have already found that Qi covers many things: infrared radiation (heat), static electricity, magnetic fields, gamma rays and other tiny particle streams. However, in Chinese Culture, Qi is also the "spirit". The Chinese character for Qi is made up of two words: one is for rice and the other is steam. When we cook rice using water and fire we see steam, so the first time we "saw" Qi was from observing steam. Therefore Qi has no shape. It is not fixed, it is something you might see, something you might smell and something you might feel.

For example, air we call "empty Qi" and the weather we call "heavenly Qi". If someone is very dignified and good, we say he has "spiritual Qi". Sometimes, when we go to a restaurant and the food is very good, we say that the chef has "very good wok Qi". Qi is also what gives us energy to live and function. When we are tired, our Qi is low. When we have lots of energy, then our Qi level is high.

When we practise Qigong, Qi flows along all the channels and acupuncture points, to balance the body. The channels in our bodies are like a motorway. When there are no blockages or traffic jams, then the Qi will move smoothly and the whole system is in balance. It is the same as the universe. All the stars and planets have their own orbit to keep the universal order. One system of Chinese horoscope prediction is based upon how the energies of the five elements interact with each other. By discovering when the energy is low, then we know we have to be careful at this time. When the energy is strong, then we can work harder and achieve more. When your Qi is strong, you can transmit it to help others who are sick. This is what Qigong masters have done for rnany years to help the sick rid themselves of disease.

Everyone has Qi but not everyone can feel or experience Qi. That does not mean it does not exist. Sometimes, people try to go too far to prove that Qi exists. I remember watching a programme on an introduction to Qigong. The Qigong master first explained the basic principles of Qigong. He said "Qi is the energy that can heal people when they are suffering from illness, and it can also affect the body...". After his explanation he told the audience in front of him and the cameramen to relax and close their eyes. He then concentrated and moved his hands towards the audience. After about three minutes he told them to open their eyes, hold the palms of their hands together and compare the lengths of the fingers on one hand compared to the other. Some found that fingers on one hand were longer than the same fingers on the other hand! Some found they had no reaction, but by the end, many people were impressed by him.

In China, some Qigong masters do the same things to prove the power of Qi. Some use Qi to make themselves taller and some transmit Qi only to their students to prove their Qi is strong. When other masters see and judge this, they say "This is not really Qigong!" If a master wants to prove his Qi is strong, he should first transmit Qi to people he does not know. If he can affect them, then this proves how strong his Qi is. Of course some people are more sensitive and some are less sensitive. If they are not sensitive, then you need to transmit more Qi to prove yourself. If you just transmit to people who you know, the audience will think it is just a trick or that you are lying to them. When a person is sitting or standing relaxed, automatically their body can become taller or parts of the body can become longer, even without Qi transmission! This just makes the sceptical person disbelieve in Qi even more.

For someone who is practising Qigong, the aim should be for health not proving their Qi. Everything else, including developing your potential comes next. So the first thing is to make yourself healthy, and this can be proven by your attitude and your appearance. If you are not healthy, people can tell. No matter how much make-up you use, you cannot hide! When you are healthy, your Qi will build up through daily practice. Finally it will be strong enough to transmit. If your Qi is not strong, then of course not everyone will be able to sense it and respond to it - so you should practise more, until you reach that level. But never try to act and lie to yourself, otherwise you will damage the image of Qigong.

Fighting
Cancer

"You have only two months to live," the doctor told the patient who had been diagnosed with cancer. There is no doubt that this is a very scary sentence. Who can be calm and accept it? Cancer is a very serious illness and considered an incurable disease. In western medicine, cancer patients will have chemotherapy and radiotherapy, even operations to get rid of the cancer. They believe that by using strong chemicals, drugs or operations that the cancer cells can be either killed or cut out.

However, no one can really guarantee that the cancer cells will not grow again somewhere else. Lately, I have been treating many cancer patients, most of whom have already had chemotherapy treatment or operations or both. So after the Qigong treatment, when I have finished working on their acupuncture points and channels and transmitting Qi to them, they find they look good and feel better. However, if the patient is still having chemotherapy or taking other medicines, then the body uses the energy from the treatment and the Qi gathered from their own Qigong practice to try and cleanse the body of toxins (including the medicine as well as the negative energy). So the next time when I see the patient, they often look tired and are weak again.

Therefore I always prefer that they either stop or complete the western treatment before I treat them. Otherwise it wastes the energy. Also, from my experience, many people who have chemotherapy or operations will have problems again later in a few years time and this time it will be even more serious. However, I see that Qigong can help. It is used widely as a treatment for cancer in China, helping the patient fight the problem by building up more Qi through exercise and relaxation. There are many Qigong hospitals where they use Qigong to treat not only cancer, but other illnesses and disease as well.

When you prac-tise Qigong, your body becomes stronger. Actually our bodies are stronger than we think and doing Qigong brings up the Qi so that you can stand the cancer. Firstly, as your Qi becomes stronger, the cancer cells will stop growing. This means that you will not be so tired and weak. More practice can improve the blood circulat-ion and make the internal organs str-ong. Even the problem areas will be stronger. If your body has fresh blood, then it can maintain the good condition of other areas in the body. In addition, the spirit will be strong so that the body can easily fight the cancer.

The problem area will then begin to heal and hard lumps will become softer and eventually disappear as the cells become normal again. But during Qigong treatment and practice, the patient must have enough patience to continue their own Qigong practice every day, even if on some days they feel weak or depressed. On these days they can do less but must not miss the practise completely. I have read of cases in China where people practice for several hours throughout the day in order to fight cancer. They know that their health is the most important thing and so devote their time and energy to getting better. In the west, people accept taking medicines or treatments more than trying to heal the illness naturally. Actually the weaker the patient feels, then the more practice they need to make them stronger, even if it is in little bits at a time.

The Qi that is gathered from practice is like a dam. It is this which is holding back the cancer cells from growing. It is also fighting to overcome them as well. Your body is relying on the Qi, rather than strong medicine or operations. This is quite the opposite of western medicine which relies on these conventional therapies. However, studies have shown that these same drugs or operations can damage healthy parts of the body as well as the diseased parts. They can also make the patient weaker and weaker until eventually they cannot survive. The cancer then grows too fast for the body to fight.

In my experience, positive results can be had through the practice of Qigong if the patient is diligent in their practice and does not give up but keeps fighting. We all have to overcome difficulties in our life and this is one of the most difficult as cancer is still considered an incurable disease. Qigong helps improve not only the body's condition but the spirit and makes the mind stronger as well in order to fight.

Bad Qigong Master

Once when I was giving a seminar in Canada, I met a lady who told me a disturbing story of a Qigong seminar she had attended in Calgary. She had read an article in a newspaper announcing that a Qigong master from China was coming to Canada. As she had always been interested in holistic teachings, particularly concerning health, she was interested to find more details. The article in the newspaper explained that Qigong could heal many different illnesses, prevented other problems in the body and was related to breathing, exercise and the mind. It also mentioned that the organiser said that it related to Shaolin Qigong. The organiser was also Chinese and this gave her more confidence to join in.

The course ran over about five weekends and quite a lot of people, both men and women, attended. The first four weekends went very well and the people had the opportunity to learn Qigong exercises and principles. The master could not speak English and therefore relied on the Chinese organiser to translate. However, on the last weekend, without any warning, the teacher was changed to another Chinese master, who was said to be also from China. The organiser explained that the original teacher had to go back to deal with some personal affairs. The attendees did not doubt this, but the new teacher seemed different from the last one, particularly in his attitude.

However, the course continued. On the last day the new master called everyone to see him in a small room individually. The lady thought that this must be a Chinese custom. One by one the people went in, but when they came out they acted a little strange. Then the lady was called and she went into the room. There was the new master sitting in a chair with a table in front of him. She sat in another chair opposite him with the table in between. The new master spoke to her in Chinese but she did not understand a word he said and there was no one else in the room to translate. After a while he got up and came closer.

Suddenly he tried to kiss her on the mouth. She was shocked and did not know how to react. Then he started to touch her. She tried to cover herself up. She had never thought that this could happen and was afraid and embarrassed. Then she was told to leave the room and soon after the course finished. She left and went home, but that night she could not sleep and kept thinking about the events and why these things had happened. After a while she got a phone call from the organiser who wanted to see her, but she could tell from his attitude that something was not right. He too had also tried to kiss her during a conversation. So from then every time the phone rang she felt nervous and apprehensive. Even today she still has some shadows of that day following her.

A few years later she met another lady who had attended the same course. She too said that she had heen accosted by the new master. When she told me this I was shocked and angry. How could people teaching Qigong do this? Fortunately, she did not lose her trust in Qigong practice and is now studying Dayan Qigong. Learning this has given her more confidence.

Qigong is getting more and more popular and I am sure that the interest in it will continue to grow. Many people benefit from it and practise Qigong to improve their health. However, some "masters'" use this opportunity to do wrong. They hurt others and damage the image of Qigong. Some use sex to attract the innocent and confuse beginners. Others may promise miracle results or healing powers within just a weekend of practice. We should not be naive when we choose a teacher. Make sure of their attitude and methods they use to teach, getting as much information and even references if you feel necessary. We are trusting this teacher to show us ways to benefit and improve our health. We do not want them to make our problem worse or as in the case of my student, make her worry and feel upset.

Tonic or Medicine

On the 28th of November 1993, I watched a programme on BBC2 television about Dr Peter Jepson Young who was dying from AIDS. The programme followed him as his symptoms changed and he explained what was happening. It was very sad. He changed from a normal, good looking young man, until he looked like a frail old man. He suffered pain, his face and legs became swollen, his body became stiff until he lost all sensation. Later he even became blind and developed cancer until finally he died. During his suffering he was treated with many medicines, and they were a heavy burden. They made him lose his hair, his teeth and made his bones so weak he could not walk. They may even have contributed to developing cancer.

AIDS or Acquired Immune Deficiency Syndrome basically causes a total breakdown of a person's immune system. They are unable to fight off the simplest of viruses or bacteria - from the common cold to flu

49

and fever. Often a simple cold can turn into pneumonia because the body is unable to fight off the germs invading it. AIDS is considered an incurable disease in the west and it is very frightening as no one really knows what causes it or how to best treat it.

However, in Chinese medicine there is no such thing as an incurable disease. Everything depends on balance. People die because their internal energy cannot balance with the external universal energy of the environment, the weather and with nature. If you can no longer follow this system, then you are eliminated. Nature follows the principles of Yin and Yang. This is Dao. So every problem must have a solution otherwise it would not exist and so in nature, any illness or disease must have something to balance it.

Qigong exercises build up your vital energy (Qi). You take the energy from the air you breathe. Air is the energy for all living things on this planet. No one can survive without it. If your Qi is strong, then your immune system will be strong. For example, one day after you have been working very hard you go home. Inside your home it is very cold and you begin to feel chilled inside. Then the next day, when you wake up you find you feel ill - you have caught a cold. If you had practised Qigong before you had gone to bed, you would perhaps not have become ill. Qigong would have brought your body back to normal by balancing it with the external environment. Practising Qigong would have created internal heat to ward off the cold as well as strengthening your immune system to fight off any infection.

Often when I treat my patients, I find that many of them expect me to give them medicine or herbs. I always say to them "You don't need medicine, you need exercise." Exercise is the best way to recuperate from illness. Sometimes, to begin with, they are sceptical of my advice, but after a week or so of practising the exercises I have shown them, they are pleased to come back and tell me how good they feel. The more they practise, they more they find that they can control and live with their pain. From that time, they start to realise the exercises can bring up their energy and so begin to practise Qigong every day.

I am sure that nobody likes to take medicines all of their life. No matter how good or effective the medicine, it still does not belong to your body as it has not been created by your body. Often, medicines have side effects which can make the patient feel even worse than they did before. You need your own energy to balance your body. The more energy you have, the less suffering you will have. If you need to always rely on medicine, then it creates a great dependency in the body. Your body can even forget how to heal itself. Sometimes the body will develop an intolerance for the medicine if taken for a long time and so you need even more or stronger medicine to help. Even if it works this time, the next time the same problem comes back, you may need even more medicine to help. Finally your cupboard will be full of medicine bottles.

We are human beings, not medicine men! Step by step, you should reduce the amount of medicine you take and let your body go back to normal and healthy. Qigong can help you build up your resistance to fight against all kinds of illnesses. There are many studies now taking place on how Qigong can help cure many kinds of illness, including AIDS, cancer, chronic illnesses such as ME and backache, and also many other kinds of internal diseases. In China, there are many hospitals devoted to Qigong healing or which have a special branch for this. The healers themselves study Qigong many hours a day to keep themselves healthy and their energy levels strong so that when they do transmit their energy, the do not become weakened or ill themselves. The patients practise exercises given to them and they have very good results.

Usually, though, these patients are not taking other forms of medicines. The reason for this is because the body views any kind of medicine as foreign and not part of its natural system. So when practising Qigong, the body will first try to rid the body of these impurities. So instead of working for the disease, the energy is taken up by trying to get rid of toxins.

I remember once when I gave a Qigong workshop for the National Conference for Cancer Self Help Groups. Many people from many different countries in Europe and further afield attended the conference. Some were suffering from cancer whilst others were looking for information or came along with friends or relatives who were ill. There was a great deal of information on offer along with different kinds of workshops and lectures. The event was very successful. Of the people who attended my workshop, some were already receiving chemotherapy or radiotherapy. Some were in quite good health, but others were not and sadly, others only had a few months left to live.

During the workshop, I introduced Qigong and taught some exercises to help them with their problems or to help prevent the problems. Some had already heard of Qigong or were already practising. They understood the need for Qigong, to make the body

strong to fight against the cancer. Other people did not know about Qigong, but had heard that Chinese methods of healing had been very successful in treating many "incurable diseases". In China millions of people practise Qigong everyday. Qigong is a way of building up your Qi to fight illness naturally.

When you are ill, it means the body has a problem that you need to get rid of, otherwise it will cause other problems. Of course, some things are only small prob-lems that you will automatically recover from in just a few days. However, if your body is too weak, then you will need other support to make you healthy. Nowadays, medicine is one solution, but medicines do not usually belong to your body. So when you take them they make you tired and bring down your energy. If the problem is serious, then medicines do not help very much. Having taken them you may even suffer from side effects such as hair loss, dry skin, loss of concentration, upset digestion, etc.

With Qigong therapy, we build up the immune system to fight the illness by building up strong Qi. Of course, with something as serious as cancer, you will need to do a lot of exercise to keep your Qi circulation strong to rid yourself of negative Qi. As you do this your internal organs, cells, arteries, etc, will become healthy. It is the same as looking after a plant. If you place it in the right environment, with fresh air, sunshine and water, then even a plant that is about to die will under the right conditions become healthy once more. Rotten leaves, branches and roots will fall away and new ones will grow back. We humans are very powerful creatures. Our bodies and minds have the ability to adapt to any difficult situation. It is only because we do not use and train this ability that we lose it. As long as we can return to nature, we will be able to maintain it.

There is a system for every living thing in the universe to follow. If you can follow it, then you will live longer, but if you go against it then you will die earlier. This is Dao. No matter what illness or disease, there must be a cure - just follow nature.

Feng Shui

In the past I look at what I have done
In the future I can overcome my past wrongs
Actually, I did not lose my way too far
I feel from today my way is right

Old Chinese saying

Changing
Your Luck

Many people at Chinese New Year ask me, "Will this year be a good year or a bad year?" Actually every year is good and also bad and depends on your horoscope.

Everybody's life goes up and down, some years are good and other are not so good, we all follow a cycle. Even every month, every day and every hour is changing. Perhaps when you are younger, your life is very good, but when you are older life is not so good; this is all individual and is different from one person to the next. However, when good luck comes you still have to work for it and take care of it, and do not use all of it.

Some people take all of their good fortune in one go and they do not put any effort into maintaining it. Then, when all the good luck has gone and bad luck follows, they find themselves so unlucky. They will say, "Oh, in the past everything was so good and now ..." Of course, the situation has changed, but you have to ask yourself if you have really tried to improve yourself? If you have not, then you should not complain about it to others. Laziness can damage your future. The Chinese say, "If you do not work hard when you are young, when you are old you will be sad."

Some people do work hard but it seems that no matter what they do, they still do not succeed. This maybe means that they have chosen something that is unsuitable for their horoscope and nature. Perhaps you would like to be the boss of your own business, however, when you get set up, it seems that you cannot get any business and the bills keep piling up. Not everyone is meant to be a leader or on their own. Some people find that they reach their best potential when they can help and assist someone else. Then that person who is the boss can take care of you and reward your good work. If you really want to improve yourself, then you have to work. It does not matter what situation you are in, you can still learn. Some people are very talented, but if you find you are not so talented, then you have to work harder.

There are certain things we cannot change, and these are pre-natal. They come form your parents and are in your genes. They follow nature or the system of society you live in, like the rules of a game we must follow. Then there are things we can change. These are post-natal. We can try our best and no matter how difficult they are, we can change them and get what we want (but these should not be immoral or illegal things).

Once there was a rich man who had a son. The son grew up well loved and protected in the care of his family. Anything that he wanted, he would get. None of the servants dared refuse him anything. His parents loved him very much, being their only child. When he grew up, his father gave him a high position in his company and so he was boss over many people. Because he was the owner's son, however, even if he made a wrong decision, no one dared to disagree with him.

Eventually his father died and left the business to his son. However, because the son had never had any obstacles in his life, he could not tell if anything was wrong with the business or not. Of course, every business must face at least one problem, even only a small mistake. However, in the case of the son, he did not know how to handle these problems, so even a small problem became big. It eventually even caused the business to collapse and close down. All of his father's hard work was lost, because he had spoiled his son. So sometimes, something so good might not always be so good. Also, something so bad may not always be so bad. Chinese say, "Making a business is difficult, but keeping that business is more difficult."

If you are not able to get what you want, do not just sit at home and complain because this will not change the situation. I always find things are not so difficult so long as you really put your heart into it. Sometimes if we think less about our own situation and try to do some good for others, this good will come back to us. But we should not just sit around and be depressed. Work for something and do not wait for luck to come. Luck comes from hard work. It may be that you cannot do it right now because your skills are not ready or the situation does not allow it, but that does not mean we should give up. For example, if you want to write a book, but do not have much time, just write a little everyday, then after a year, you will have your book. But if you are only enthusiastic at the beginning and lose interest after a few days, then you will not succeed and never get what you want. "Laziness can damage your future." Your future depends on you working for it.

What is Feng Shui?

Recently I spoke to a lady who wanted to learn Feng Shui and she was very enthusiastic about it. She asked me where she could learn it and learn it quickly. At the age of 56 and on a low income, she wanted a skill she could use to make more money, as she did not make enough to support herself. I felt sorry for her and explained that it takes many years of study and that you also need a good teacher to study with. You can not just learn a little skill and then go and use it on someone's home because you might even make the situation worse.

She then said that she had seen an advertisement for a Feng Shui seminar in which the teacher charged £200 for a weekend course and which claimed that afterwards you could use the skill on people's homes to do Feng Shui surveys. This is very scary. How can you learn 2000 years of skill in just one weekend? I believe the instructor is from America. Although I am not saying a non-Chinese person cannot learn a Chinese skill, I saw that this particular instructor mixes up his teachings with Greek and even Gypsy culture and still claims that it is Feng Shui.

Feng Shui is a Chinese skill and should not be mixed up with western skills. If you really know Feng Shui then you know that it is a complete system and once you mix it up it becomes something else. Another point is that Feng Shui requires a lot of calculations. It is more than just moving furniture and changing the colour of the rooms or hanging wind chimes. In Feng Shui, we call doing this Luan Tou. Luan Tou relates to objects and substance, such as mountains and water. The other part is Li Qi and this is also important. Li Qi relates to the cycle of Qi for every sixty and twenty years as well as every year, every month, every day and every hour. For example, one of the things that Li Qi can tell you is how the Ju Men and Lian Zhen Stars can damage the health of the home owner, make them ill and even result in accidents and cause the death of elderly people.

Some people do not believe in Feng Shui and think that it is only based upon superstitious beliefs. However, Feng Shui is also based on the Yijing, the He Tu Pre-natal Bagua and the Lo Shu Post-natal Bagua and uses many calculations of the Chinese compass, like the twenty-four mountains. Your mathematics have to be good if you really want to have high level Feng Shui skill because we also need to know how to calculate a person's Ba Zi (Chinese horoscope) as well.

There is also the high level skill of Qi Men Dun Jia which talks about eight doors and includes opening, resting, growing, injury, blocking, imagination, death and fright. This skill also enables you to calculate direction and timing for events that can happen. In the past the emperors of China used this skill during wars to find out how their enemies would attack or move their armies and how to conceal themselves and how to attack. Now we use it in our houses to find out how to catch the best Qi.

Feng Shui is a very powerful life skill which can enhance our lives, but if used in the wrong way it can also damage the Qi as well.

Five Yellow Star - Dantien of Your Home

Qi is the most important thing for all types of Chinese skill. It does not matter if you are talking about health, eating or living. We all use Qi to measure the quality of the subject. Many people like to describe Qi as being energy. Somehow, it is more than this. It also relates to feeling, spirit and quality. If you say somebody has good Qi, apart from saying that this person has very good spirit, you can also say that this person has good charm. So Qi is not only related to energy but is also related to how you feel. It is the essence for everything.

Chinese say that Qi is equivalent to air. We all need air to live. Good air gives you good Qi, while bad air gives you bad Qi. When you live in a good area with lots of fresh air and plenty of space, then you will automatically be healthier and smarter. People living in an area where the air is bad are all the time taking in negative Qi, and so they will be confused and unhealthy. They may even have strange thinking and behaviour. So we all rely on good Qi to make ourselves healthy and balanced.

In our body, when we take in the good air through the nose, breathing in and out and exchanging the air from the lungs, we also take the essence of the air. This is then retained in our body. The air coming into our body is not just oxygen. It is much more than this. It also contains a lot of energy from nature. This energy is stored at the centre

of our bodies in an area we call the Dantien. This area is located approximately an inch below the navel.

The more energy you take in, the larger area your Dantien will cover. This stored essence or Qi will be used when our body really needs it. So when we work hard or when we are tired, suddenly we will find that we have more energy to use. However, if we do not use this energy, it will stay stored and help us to be healthier and live longer. This is why we have a method to develop the Qi which is called Qigong. Qi means vital energy and gong means work. Qigong helps us work for the energy so that we can live healthier and longer lives.

Much of the Qigong we see is very gentle and easy. We often come across standing postures, called Zhan Zhuang. This is where we stand still, relax the whole body and let the Qi sink to the Dantien. There are many different postures that one can use. Qigong also has another simple method which is movement. This helps us to open the channels and acupuncture points and also brings more Qi to the Dantien. So all the methods of Qigong are concerned with bringing Qi back to the Dantien.

The Dantien is a very important part of the body. Apart from the Dantien, the internal organs are very important for maintaining the internal energy. There are five major organs: heart, liver, kidney, spleen and lungs. If any of these organs has a problem, it will affect the Dantien. The Dantien is like a general and the internal organs are like the soldiers. Therefore, if someone has a problem with their heart but their Dantien Qi is still strong, then they can still survive much longer. If their Dantien Qi is weaker, that will be a problem.

Some people who have a heart problem live longer and some live shorter lives. This is because of their Dantien Qi. Sometimes when we are ill, if we practise Qigong, then we can recover much more quickly or can cope much better with the problem. In modern society, people who have health problems usually will take drugs which will make us tired, weaker and older. Some will find it hard to survive.

Practising Qigong can help you develop the Dantien Qi and maintain the five organs. Sometimes, if you know which organ has a problem, then you can do something to help this organ particularly. You can do this by doing your Qigong practice facing the direction which corresponds to that organ. The liver connects with the east, kidneys to the north, heart to the south, lungs to the west and spleen with the southwest and northeast. In addition, you can even practise during a certain time of the day as each of the organs corresponds to the twelve Chinese hours of the day. They are liver (1-3am), lung (3-5am), spleen (7-9am), heart (11-1pm) and kidney (5-7pm). So you can choose the direction and the time of practise which will most benefit your health.

There is also another way to help your condition and this is through your own home. The entrance to your home is where the strongest energy will come. So the entrance will connect with the directions and also the five major organs of your body. If you have a good entrance facing in the direction of east, then your liver energy will be stronger. However, if the entrance to your home is somehow blocked or cluttered or there are road works outside, then this energy is negative and will affect your organs in this way. So a good entrance is very important to bring the good energy into the home for your health.

Our houses are equivalent to our bodies. The major entrance is comparable to our nose and mouth. What we breathe in and what food we eat affects the condition of our body. Therefore, the inside of a house also has a Dantien. The Dantien of a house is at the middle of the house. Anything that affects the Dantien of the house will also affect the energy of the body. In Feng Shui this is called, Ng Wong Sing,

69

and means Five Yellow Star which relates to the post-natal bagua in which the number five star is at the centre.

The Ng Wong Sing should not be disturbed. If there is decorating going on in this area or if there are rubbish bins or something else obstructing it, like a wardrobe or something large, then this will disturb the Dantien of the house. Similarly, it will also affect the health of the people living there, break up relationships, affect their job or even worse. It can cause accidents, injury or death. So you should find the Dantien of your house and make sure it is alright, then it can help improve your condition.

The Feng Shui of Bruce Lee

The news of Brandon Lee's death shocked the whole world, especially all the fans of his father, Bruce Lee. At the time, the newspapers and magazines often mentioned Brandon because of the movies he had starred in. Many people at that time were looking for his father's shadow in him.

When I was little and living in Hong Kong, Bruce Lee was my hero. All the Hong Kong people liked him. He proved that a small Chinese person could be strong and his fighting skill showed that martial arts should be direct and not decorated. In particular, his muscular build impressed everyone. His back, when he spread his arms, looked as if it had wings. His facial expressions and his charisma, no one can forget. During the seventies, the world's attention was upon him. Television, newpapers and magazines alike reported stories about him and anything with his name on it would sell. At that time, many martial arts clubs become full of new students overnight. To the martial arts world, it was like a miracle.

So when suddenly news of his death came, nobody could believe it. Even now no one is completely sure how he died. It is still a debated upon secret. Now, twenty years later, his own son has died in a filming accident. This has made many people think about both Brandon Lee and his father, Bruce Lee. It has been reported that before he died, he said he felt that the demon that had killed his father was now following him. Some people even said it was this demon that took his life. This created a mystical side to Brandon Lee's death. However, on the other side of the world in Hong Kong, people had another explanation for Brandon Lee's death. They said it was a result of his family's Feng Shui.

Feng Shui has become very popular in the West and it is easy to walk into a book shop and find many books on the subject. Feng means wind and Shui means water. Wind and water are the major elements that affect our lives. They are the basic energies that are connected to our environment. If your environment and house is not good, then this can affect your health and finances and relationships. A good house has good energy and a bad house has bad energy.

In Feng Shui, if we only deal with the energy of a house, we call this Yang House Feng Shui. As a balance, we also have Yin House Feng Shui and this relates to the energy of a burial site. After a person dies, we bury them in a grave. This grave also has energy and it is this Yin House Feng Shui that will tell the energy that will then affect the deceased person's offspring. If the ancestor is buried in a place with good energy, then it will bring good luck to the children, maybe they will become famous even or very rich. In the past, Yin House

Feng Shui was used only for an Emperor to find a burial site that would ensure his bloodline would contine to rule and be properous. Traditional Feng Shui is therefore very important to Chinese people.

A Feng Shui master once informed Bruce Lee's family that their Yin House Feng Shui was not good. However, the advice was ignored and today we can see the result. We can also see that Bruce Lee's siblings also are affected with marital problems which ended in divorce and remarriage. The Feng Shui master said that Bruce Lee's father, Lee Hoi Chuen was buried in the wrong place. Lee Hoi Chuen was a very famous actor in the Chinese opera and also movies. He was a very well known figure in Hong Kong and was the impetus of Bruce Lee's beginning in movies as a child. Bruce's father died during the Japanese war when they bombed Canton. Next to his father's grave was the grave of a young child who had died in an accident. So it was not a very lucky symbol for Bruce Lee's father.

To fix the problem, the master suggested building a wall between the graves to block the energy from the adjacent grave. However, the Lee family did not accept what he had said. Perhaps it is understandable as at this time, the world was rapidly changing and traditional values and skills were considered old fashioned. This was the time of the Americans landing on the moon, western medicine and philosophy booming across the world and the beginning of the computer age. Science was like god and could get you what you wanted. It seemed a small thing to think about the grave of someone who had long ago ceased to exist. How could a grave affect the lives of living people? People were more interested in which car was the fastest, who had the newest television and which stereo had the best sound. People were more interested in material things and possessions, including Hong Kong, even though China was in the middle of its Cultural Revolution.

After Bruce Lee's death, no one remembered the words of the Feng Shui master but many stories about his death emerged. One said that his Chinese name was ill fated. In Chinese Bruce Lee was called Little Dragon. At that time he was living in Kowloon Tong, Hong Kong. However, Kowloon Tong meant the Pool of Nine Dragons, so how could one small dragon compete against nine dragons, people asked.

One story also dealt with the Feng Shui of the Hong Kong house that Bruce Lee was living in at the time of his death. They said that it was like a coffin lid because of the shape of the roof. So when you entered the house, it was like entering a coffin itself.

Another rumour was about his last film, "Game of Death". They said that this film's name brought him bad luck because it connected him with death. The film itself was finished while Bruce Lee lay in his grave. I have also heard a story that after his death when his coffin was being transported from Hong Kong to America, that it cracked due to the air pressure in the plane's cargo hold. So when he arrived in America, they needed to change his coffin… not a lucky thing to do.

We can also see that Bruce Lee's health was beginning to deteriorate. In the movie, *Enter the Dragon*, we can see his face is quite dark in comparison to his earlier times. That dark colour reflected the state of his health, being connected with the kidneys. It is said in Chinese medicine, that when the face and forehead turns black, then death is not far away, that luck has gone. The kidneys are very important organs as they store our energy and Jing (sexual energy and sperm). If the kidneys become damaged or very weak, a person will develop back problems, suffer from tiredness and have puffiness under their eyes. They may even become dizzy, forgetful and their face will turn dark.

Many unhappy things happened to Bruce Lee. Although he worked very hard at his martial arts and philosophy, he did not even live to see his most famous film, *Enter the Dragon*. It is very sad. The Chinese say, "Big trees will catch more wind." With all the attention that was being focused on him, it was sure that anything that did happen to him, good or bad, would be big.

In traditional Chinese Feng Shui, when a person died, the family then had to find a good place to bury them. This would bring good luck to the family's offspring, as well as bringing the ancestor himself peaceful rest. Like a tree that has strong and deep roots, the fruit that it bears will naturally be big and sweet and ripen to maturity. Alternatively, a grave with the wrong Feng Shui will bring the wrong energy to the offspring and can damage their health, business, affect their marriage and lives. Therefore, those who could afford to do so would already have found a good Feng Shui master to locate a good location gravesite for them, before their death.

This is, however, only Yin House Feng Shui. We must also consider the house that we live in which is Yang House Feng Shui. One of the most important things is the environment outside the house. It should not be too close to a busy road nor near any construction or building works as this can affect the health and relationships of those in the house. The house itself should be in good condition, with things tidy and in order.

The colours and the facing directions of the doors and windows should also be taken into consideration and matched with the horoscope of the people who live there. Positions of furniture and good air and correct light are also important. These are the basic elements of Feng Shui and should all be considered properly, otherwise it could affect also your business and fortunes.

How you decorate your main entrance to your home, your bedroom, dining room, kitchen, toilet and garden will all affect you. Every year the energy of the universe changes, so you must also consider these changing energies. One year money may come from the north but the next year it will change and so you may have to move furniture or put a light in a particular area to help. Your house affects your health, your work, even your mental well being, so the importance of good Feng Shui cannot be igonored.

People with good fortunes have good Feng Shui houses. People who have lost their postions or who have had their businesses run down or who have had marriage difficulties, all have something wrong with the Feng Shui of either their home or business. The history of Feng Shui is very deep and is a very complex and profound skill. It is not witchcraft but relies on many calculations, using a compass and other methods to find the right energy and right solution. Feng Shui is a skill which can help enhance and in some cases save people's lives and business.

Hong Kong's China Bank Building

When I last visited Hong Kong, one particular building was always being talked about in the news, Feng Shui books and magazines and by Feng Shui masters all over. So I decided to go and have a look at it myself. The building is a very strong and powerful building and represents the power of Chinese money in Hong Kong. You may have even seen pictures of the building yourself. It is the China Bank building. The position of the building is just right to catch energy from all the directions.

The period of the years dating 1984 to 2003 is the "Seven Win" period, which means the good number for this period will be seven. As both the directions east and west are related to seven, all this is good for the China Bank building. The building also has a very sharp shape, like a knife, with long antennae on the top which makes it one of the most prominent buildings in the area. This means that China will do a lot of business and have a lot of communication with other countries. The sharp edge means that it cuts the business from the people around it.

The building's facade is made to look like mirrors and so it reflects back to the other buildings surrounding it. This makes its position very outstanding and gives it a leading position. These can also be used to reflect any negative energy from itself. Any companies doing business with the China Bank will be protected and taken care of. However, if you do not do business with them, then you will have to go on your own and then they become like a knife to hurt you. People living around the China Bank building will also be affected by its stong presence. They may suffer heart problems and nervous disorders. It is because of these things that the building has been critised by so many people. Because its shape is so strong, it will cause a lot of people to suffer in Hong Kong and the city will not easily be peaceful.

In Feng Shui, buildings and also mountains belong to different elements which represent different energy. There are five elements:

earth, metal, water, wood and fire – and the China Bank building represents fire because of its triangular shape. This is good for activitiy and quick business. A wood element building is very upright, like a tree growing upward. If you live in that area, the building will seem like a mountain and the people there will be gentle and good at studying. They will be well educated and good natured. A water building or mountain will cause the people who live near to be half active and half gentle and calm. They will be quick minded and good for delicate work, like electronics or computer work.

A metal building or mountain is round or semicircular on top. It is very strong and strict. People in that area will be well organised and work with machines. An earth building or mountain is very flat, like a big piece of land. It will be able to store a lot of energy and the people who stay in that area will represent rich, long lasting things. From this we can see that when we are deciding on where to live, that we must not just look at the inside of a home, but also the surrounding area and what the buildings or mountains are like. You should find the ones that suit your nature. If you see a building that is broken or damaged, this will affect your Qi and can even affect your relationships. It is not good to live there. You can also look at the people who live in that area, whether they are good or bad, whether they are healthy or unhealthy, settled or unsettled, and this will help you to judge that area. It is the same as growing a plant. You need to find the right soil and direction which is best for that plant.

Culture & Philosophy

If two people are one in heart, mountains and oceans cannot separate them. If two men do not share common ideals, there will be great distance between them though they stand side by side. This is why some people travel across mountains and waters to meet and others never make contact with each other though they stay together.

Old Chinese saying

Cause
and Effect

The Chinese believe that everything in life follows the rule of cause and effect. It is something that has become almost hereditary and is told to children from the day they are born. I still remember my mum would tell us that if we were bad or did any immoral things, then we would be reincarnated as dogs, cows or horses. A cow or horse has a particularly hard life as they spend all of their energy serving humans every day until they die. Although many people do not believe in reincarnation or cause and effect or any religion, we must all wait until the end when we see the results of our lives to really find out.

Myself, I believe everything we do must have an effect which will eventually come out. Even if we do not see it on the outside, it will be on the inside, maybe in ourselves or in our relatives or someone else. For example, someone who has done many bad things might only live a short life, they might die when they are only 30 or 40 years old. Some other bad people may not have any children or they might have something happen to their parents or maybe their husband or wife might leave them. Whatever happens, he or she will have to face it.

Perhaps you know someone who has done many bad things, but still they live in a big house and drive a nice car and have money to do whatever they want. You might think, "This is not right, what happened to the rule of cause and effect?". But actually, how much do you know about this person? Does he sleep well at night, does he feel good or does he have pains or feel ill? Maybe he is angry a lot or unhappy. No matter how good you look on the outside, you can not hide what is in your heart and the state of your health.

If you practise Qigong regularly, inside you make yourself healthy, but have you noticed how your nature changes the longer you practise. You or maybe the pople around you notice that you are more easy going, relaxed, good tempered and have developed a kinder heart. This attitude your father cannot even change. Only when your health changes will your heart change and then your nature will change automatically.

Sometimes people will try and take our advantage. There was a case where a person went to a special school to study Qigong and martial arts. However, after learning just some of the skill and even before reaching a good standard, he left and changed some of the forms and even said bad things about his teacher. So he not only betrayed the source of his skill but also damaged it. It was not long before the person's students became ill and even he himself had health problems. Outside these people may look good, but inside they are completely different. You should not get upset over them. Heaven is very fair and everybody will get their result. You might not be able to see it, but life is a circle and so we should concentrate to maintain our principles and heart. Then everything will be balanced in the end.

The
Donkey

Once upon a time there was a father and son who were taking a donkey to sell at the market. As they walked along the road leading the donkey, they came to a crossroads and heard someone laughing at them.

"How stupid!" a man called out, "Why not ride the donkey instead of walking!" The father and son thought he was right, so the father let his son ride the donkey while he walked alongside.

After a while they came to another road. Here there were some other people. When the people saw them, they started laughing and said, "Look! That son does not respect his father. He rides the donkey and lets his father walk!" Again the father and son decided that the people were right, so they both decided to ride the donkey.

Along the way they passed another road and there they met yet another group of people who were very angry. "How can you hurt your donkey like that. Two people are too much for the donkey's back to take!" At this the father and son realised these people were right, so again they changed what they were doing.

When they arrived at the market, all the people turned to look at them and started laughing, this time even harder than the people before. The father and son had tied the donkey's legs to a pole and had carried it upside down to the market so that it could rest.

This story tells us that we can easily listen and follow other people's advice, especially when what they say sounds reasonable. There are often many ways to solve a problem or complete a task. However, you need to find the way that is best for yourself and stick with it. Maybe some ways are a little slower or a bit more complicated, but if you go this way then you might even learn more. Today, we often use calculators because they are fast but on the other side, we use our minds less and less to think and calculate. Our brains then may not work as efficiently as before. It is the same with writing. More and more, computers take over the task of actually writing. So although this is more convenient, it may also mean that eventually we may not know how to write with a pen and our handwriting will not be so good. In the past, writing was not only a means of communication, it was also an art. The very way in which a person held a brush to write and how the ink flowed onto the paper was an expression of themselves. Calligraphy was an art form that also helped balance and calm the mind.

Some people may criticise the way you do something, especially when you are successful or have some advantage. Then there will always be people who are jealous of you and who try to put you down or stop you. But we should not bother for these small things. We should know our direction and although it is fine to listen to other people's advice, we still at the end have to make up our minds what is best for us. I remember my teacher once said, "In a chicken farm all the chicken ate rice and were very happy, but once someone put a small worm on the ground. One of the chickens saw the worm and rushed over to pick it up. When the other chickens realised what had happened, they began to chase it and fight for the worm." Every obstruction in life that you overcome will make you a stronger and more mature person.

Life is very interesting. The older you get the more interesting it looks. You should not worry about other people's business or about problems you cannot solve. All you can do is face them. Always remember there are so many ways to overcome your problems, not just one. When you look back you will find that in the past you did such silly things, but without these silly things you would not grow up and become more balanced. No one is perfect.

Five Colours Make You Blind

"Five colours make you blind.

Five tones make you deaf.

Five tastes make you taste nothing.

Over ambition hurts the animals, makes you lose your balanced heart.

You become crazy, looking for wealth.

Material things make you corrupt.

A gentleman and Daoist concentrates on his Dantien and not on his visions.

He leaves variety and goes for the simple."

This comes from the **Dao De Jing** by Lao Zi and is one of China's most famous Daoist works. If you can understand this fully, then you will have a high level.

"Five colours make you blind." The five colours are green, red, yellow, white and blue. They relate to the Chinese philosophy's five elements which are wood, fire, earth, metal and water. These are the basic elements which make up the world. Some people ask about air. Actually air equals Qi and is all around us so it is not seen as a distinct element. Wood relates to the liver and the colour green. Fire is connected to the heart and the colour red. Earth connects to the spleen and the colour yellow. Water connects to the kidneys and the colour blue. They all relate to our health.

Today, people watch too much television which has so many colourful pictures and patterns. Magazines and many books too have extremely colourful designs in order to try and tempt us to buy them. However, these can confuse us and even make us dizzy. The longer you are in an extremely colourful environment, the more your eyes will be affected. Eventually, you will lose the sensations of the natural colours. In particular, children today watch too much television, play TV games or use the computer too much or too long. Because their eyes are still developing, their eyes can lose their sensitivity and focus. In the end, they will end up having to wear glasses. Once you begin wearing glasses, it is difficult to get rid of them. You should be able to feel when your eyes have had too much and are tired.

"Five tones make you deaf." Chinese music is based upon five tones, different from western music that is based upon eight tones. These tones are Kung, Shen, Guou, Tze, Yeu and from these tones it is possible to make many melodies. Nowadays, however, there is so much noise everywhere. Traffic, telephones, radios, television, airplanes, even people themselves. This noise can also become a pollution and affect our health. It is very hard to find a quiet place, somewhere without noise. Even in the countryside there are many people doing work or even leisure activities, such as boating, which cause more noise and spoil the natural environment.

On trains and buses, you can see people listening to their personal stereos which should be quiet. However, many people listen to them so loudly that other passengers can easily hear the music

coming through the headphones and are disturbed. I do not know how people can stand this as I am sure that they are able to hear quite well. Once a DJ came to me and said that he had suffered a heart attack. He asked if there was anything I could do for him. Almost every evening, he spent playing "heavy" music for people to dance to. Also his hearing had definitely been damaged because of doing this night after night. Our ears connect with our kidneys. Kidneys are water and if water is weak, fire will be strong. Therefore, he had heart problems because the heart belongs to the fire element and there was no corresponding water element to balance the heart fire.

Today, if you want a peaceful and quiet place to live, you will have to spend a lot of money to find such a place. But if you are used to listening to music and suddenly, there is no music and other noise, you will find you cannot stand it and be bored. This means that your hearing has lost some of its sensitivity.

"Five tastes make you taste nothing." Sour, bitter, sweet, spicy, and salty are the five tastes. These also connect with the five elements and five major internal organs. For example, if somone likes eating salty food, but eats too much, it will affect his kidneys. Drinking too much alcohol which is considered a bitter taste, will affect the liver. Nowadays, children eat too many sweets and this affects their stomach which is also connected to the spleen. This can cause them to lose their appetite which will affect their growth.

"Over ambition hurts the animals, makes you lose your balanced heart. You become crazy, looking for wealth." In the past, people needed to hunt for food to live, but now you can just go to the supermarket and buy whatever you want. You do not need to hunt animals. Today, animals are killed with modern weapons and so the animals have little chance of surviving. Because their natural habitats are also being eroded by man, they also have less space and food to survive on. The animals lose and humans continue to expand. This will affect the balance of nature and so in the end, it will be humans fighting with humans for a place to live. In the past, hunters hunted to live, not for money or fun or out of passion. Today, it is just the opposite and this attitude will definitely damage the balance of the heart. The mind will go too far and become crazy, because passion is never satisfied.

It is the same with "looking for wealth and material things." Things like money, jewels, gold and silver are just many of the things people desire. If anyone only likes to make money and everything they do is for this purpose, they will lose their balance and will become corrupt. They will be unable to maintain their own order. To be honest, we can not take money with us after we die. Money is for using. Rich people may have more possessions than poorer people, but it does not mean they are more contented or more respected by other people.

Chinese people say, "Concentrate on money, lose friendship." This is very true. Many people before running a business together were good friends but after some time, they split up. You can see this case anywhere in the world. Now we live in the modern society. It is not like the past where we have to hunt or fight to survive. Everything is ordered and we have laws and rules to protect everyone. Of course, we still need money to run everything and keep order, but if you miss the meaning of money and are just crazy to make money to satisfy your ambitions, eventually, when those ambitions fail, you will lose your balance.

I always say that money is for using. The more you use, the more it will come back. It is like breathing, we cannot only breathe in, we must also breathe out, otherwise we will die. The more you breathe out, the more you can breathe in. But you should also know what is important to use the money for, to know your direction, otherwise, you will waste your breath.

When your mind constantly keeps looking for entertainment, colours, sounds, tastes and passion, then it will become saturated. Eventually you will lose the sensations for all and your body will not be healthy and your life will be shortened. Qigong is a healing exercise that can help balance our mind and bodies. However, if we do not let go of these external things, we will always find it difficult to concentrate on our exercise. Maybe you will even stop in the middle of practising or meditation because the mind has so many "colours".

Many Qigong practictioners too are looking for their own "colours": how to use the mind to direct Qi, how to heal others, how to open the Sky Eye. They never think about the correct attitude for practising Qigong. The correct attitude for practising Qigong is to let go and empty your mind. This is more important than learning the techniques of Qigong. Although there are many different styles and kinds of Qigong, their goal is the same: to make you healthy, balanced, clear, empty. Eventually you will become part of the universe and will live longer.

So when we practise Qigong or go about our lives, we should be clear and centred. "A gentleman or Daoist concentrates on his Dantien" and should not be distracted by the five colours. In daily life, sitting, walking, talking and eating, you should be calm and keep yourself balanced by wanting less, by "leaving variety and going for the simple".

Mok Dai Mouh

Once my son, Anthony, asked me to tell him a story. I thought for a moment then sang him a song in Chinese. The song went, "There was once a man named Mok Dai Mouh (which means Big Hair and Mok is his surname). Every day he lay in bed waiting for the chance to be a little lazy, a little bit crazy, he never shaved his beard, even gambled as well ..."

When Anthony heard this he said, "I don't believe that is a real song, you made it up". I smiled and told him it was a song written by a famous Hong Kong singer, Sam Hui, who is now retired. He said, "I still don't believe you." So to prove it I turned on the CD player and played him the song. He was very surprised. Ever since then, he has liked this song very much.

The song says, there was once a man named Mok Dai Mouh. Every day he lay in bed waiting for a chance to be a little lazy, a little bit crazy, he never shaved his beard, even gambled as well! Then one day he went to a Daoist temple named Wong Tai Sin. Everyone in Hong Kong knows this temple and people like to go and worship the Daoist god, Wong Tai Sin, in the hope that he will tell them how to

overcome their difficulties. Everyone in Hong Kong believes that Wong Tai Sin can really help and give them direction.

So Mok Da Mouh followed this traditional way to discover his future and what he should do. What he did we call "Kau Tsin" which means, "Asking for a note". This note we call "Tsin" and "Kau" means, "asking for". This note is marked on a stick and is similar to an Yijing prediction. Each stick has a number on it and each number relates to a poem. Each poem tells a story and tells you about your situation. Usually, people do not understand what the poems mean, so there is always someone there who is responsible for translating the poem, but usually you have to pay them to do this.

Mok Dai Mouh did not understand his Tsin's meaning so he went to have it translated. The man said, "This Tsin means you should look for a job straight away. Everyone should know their own talent and work hard at it. Then you will have your future." So Mok Dai Mouh listened to what the man at the temple told him and found a simple job. From this low position, he worked hard and eventually rose up to a higher position. Eventually he even worked hard enough to have his own business. In the end, he had his own house and even a Mercedes Benz car as well. By the time he had success, he had grown old. However, at the same time, he looked at his son, Mok Yee Mouh (which means Two Hair Mok). He also lay in bed and did nothing all day long. He saw that his son was lazy. So he told him how he had become successful... with hard work. Then the song ends.

This is a very good story for young people and children. We are always easily jealous of other people's success and we do not see all their hard work behind the success. I always think, if you work hard when you are young and have more energy, then when you are older, you can plan to enjoy your life and take it easy. Otherwise, if you enjoy and play too much when you are young, you will lose your enthusiasm for your future. You will then complain and moan to other people and never look at yourself to see if the problem really is you.

Then it will be too late. When you are older and want to fight for your future, you will find out it is too late. So personally, I think I should work hard when I am younger. Then, after seven or ten years, I can enjoy life more and take things a little easier. I can let go and let other people who have some potential take charge, then the Tse Qigong Centre and Qi Magazine can keep going forever.

Nature is God

I do not follow any particular religion, but I respect other people and their beliefs. A friend of mine once said, "I will worship in any temple I visit because I respect them, like you respect other people's skill."

I find that this is a very good attitude. In China there are many temples and monasteries. When we go to visit them, we should pay our respects and bow and worship the gods there, even if they do not belong to your own religion. You are showing your respect to the people whose religion it is, to their culture and their beliefs which have been passed down from their ancestors for many generations. Most religions have a long history. They give a lot of thought to how you should behave, to your direction in life. I respect all good religions and philosophies, particularly if they can help you to balance your mind and help calm the internal body. Usually they have very good rules which tell you how to behave and teach you how to be a good person. For example, they may tell you not to tell lies, not to be lazy, not to steal or go against your parents. They tell you to help others, to be honest and loyal.

These are good things for all of us, no matter which religion it is that says them. Having a good religion or philosphy usually helps to balance your mind, your behaviour and gives you a good heart. No matter how badly you behave, you will not go too far. Most religions believe that there is something maintaining the balance of the universe, looking over us all. When you do good things you get a good result and if you do something bad, then you are punished in some way. You receive the results you deserve and when you die, you might go to heaven or you might go to hell. These religious beliefs help to maintain society and keep it balanced.

This "something", that maintains the world we live in and the universe is usually called god. Most religions believe in one god and so it is easy for believers from one religion to oppose those of another religion because they do not have the same belief or believe in the same god. Sometimes I think that all the gods of different religions might all be the same, only it is that the religions themselves come from different cultures and backgrounds. Thousands and thousands of years ago people spread out all over the world. They did not know each other, but they all believed there was something controlling nature that controlled the weather and environment around them. Their beliefs were based on what they saw and found around them.

For example, when it was a nice day, people believed that "god" was in a good mood, but if there were storms, heavy rains and flooding or no rain at all, then "god" was angry and was punishing them. However, today science is very advanced, and we understand a lot more about nature and the weather and why things change and happen. When something is not right, nature will react to try and release the problem and to regain its balance overall. If it is too hot, nature will try and produce rain, and if it is too cold, it will try and create more heat through the sun. Thus, we have different seasons. We also have water, fire, the mountains and rivers and the plants and the animals. Everything is quite balanced. All this comes from the power and wonder of nature. Some people might call this a powerful intelligence or a wonderful god. Or maybe god is nature and nature is god.

Six Weathers

British people like to travel in the summer and around July and August, they will set off to find more sun. Most people in Britain like sunny, warm weather rather than the rain and cold. However, not everyone can afford to go abroad to places like Spain, Italy or France so they travel instead to Devon or Cornwall on the coast. When they get there, they enjoy the sunshine and sit on the beach. Going on holiday is also a way of taking a break from work and relaxing. In the winter, people also like to get away from the cold weather and so may travel to places like Australia, Hawaii or other tropical climates. Some people will even live in two different places, going to where it is very warm in the winter and returning back to their other home during the summer. This is very common for many elderly people.

So, is it good for a person to always travel to warmer climates and avoid the cold weather altogether? The answer is not really. If the weather is always good, you might enjoy it very much, but your body will slowly lose its sensitivity and its ability to balance and adapt to difficulty. Your body should be able to adjust to many different situations, but if it is never too hot or too cold, then you can easily become ill because the body loses its ability to adapt. So although the changes in the weather affects us, it can also help us by making us stronger.

In the winter, most people will put on many clothes: a heavy coat, gloves, scarves, etc, as they are afraid of catching a chill and becoming sick. They try to keep their body as warm as possible wherever they go. However, even when the weather is slightly warmer, many people will still dress the same and so do not let their bodies get used to a different situation. This is not the best thing for you as your body will become over protected. It will become like plants in a green house which, if they are exposed to the outside, can die. We need to be able to withstand different weather and temperatures.

I once heard of one famous doctor of Traditional Chinese Medicine say, "I do not suggest that people eat too much high nutrition food as this is not good for the body. The best thing to do is practise Taijiquan or Qigong." I totally agree with him. If you eat highly nutritious food or even take Chinese herbs like ginseng all the time, you will probably consider yourself very healthy. Actually, you may be very ill. The Chinese say, "A weak body does not like high energy food." This is because too yin cannot stand strong yang. The same as if we would try to breathe pure oxygen, we would be poisoned.

According to Chinese medicine, there are six weathers – wind, summer heat, wet, dry, cold and fire. Too much wind will damage your liver and gall bladder, affecting the blood circulation, making you nervous and your skin dry. Wind belongs to the element wood. If you stay in an area with too much wind, you may easily have these problems.

Too much heat in the summer does not happen often in Britain but it can easily be the case in countries like Africa, India and southern China. It can affect your heart, making you feel dizzy and faint. When your heart beats fast, you will sweat but this sweat will have no taste. Usually sweat has a salty taste to it. This weather belongs to the fire element.

If it is too wet it can affect your spleen and stomach and also your appetite. You will have a bad smell from your breath and body and can suffer from arthritis, aching joints and muscles. Wet belongs to the element earth.

If it is too dry, it will affect your lungs. This will make you cough, your face to be pale and you may have breathing difficulty, with pressure on your chest. This can also make your skin dry and cause depression. This type of weather belongs to the element metal.

Too much cold will affect your back, causing backache and damaging your kidneys. This will make you feel tired, make you lose your hair or make it go grey. You will feel dizzy and your face will be dark and your bones will be weak and ache. You will also have puffiness under your eyes. Cold belongs to the element water.

Too much fire means that it is too hot, but this is different from summer heat. This weather will make your heart beat fast, making you feel angry and bad tempered. You will also put on weight, sweat a lot and tire easily. You will easily lose interest in doing things.

As you can see, these six weathers can affect your health and change your emotions. A doctor of Chinese medicine can diagnose what you are suffering from by looking at your face, your skin, tongue and behaviour. In contrast, your internal body has six conditions when ill and these include, excess fire, excess dryness, excess cold, etc. These conditions are caused by imbalances in the body. Once your body has regained its balance, you will be healthy.

Nature is very cruel and eliminates anything that is weak and keeps the best. In this way, everything remains balanced. If you can understand nature, you can use it a lot.

Martial Arts

High level skill looks easy
but is based on a lot of
practice underneath.

Michael Tse

A Good
Martial
Artist

When we study martial arts, it is not just for learning fighting. If so, this is the wrong concept. The founder of Daoism, Lao Zi, said, "*Fighting is a very unlucky thing. We should only use fighting when we have no choice. If you have to use it, it must be the last resort. Once you use it, try to use only the minimal force. When you have completed your purpose, you should stop. Do not treat fighting as a wonderful thing.*"

The Chinese character for martial arts literally means "stop fighting". That is exactly the way of the martial artist. We learn it for self-defence, not for bullying other people. We should not use it the wrong way to harm other people without reason. That is like a country who needs everybody to be safe and protected. So they send police out into the streets to avoid people taking advantage of others. If anybody did take advantage, then it is the resonsibility of the police to stop them, not punish them. When we study martial arts, it is the same meaning. We try and stop the people from hurting us. If you can handle someone who attacks you and who is stronger, then it means your skill is not bad. If you can handle several people who even have weapons, it means your martial art skill is very good. This is using martial arts properly, for self defence.

Today, people study martial arts for self training, discipline, physical and fighting skill training. However, a good martial arts teacher will also teach you philosophy, morality, how to respect the seniors and how to take care of the juniors. They should also teach you how to take care of your health as well. At the end, you will be a good person, with good health and good fighting skill.

Children today are not really taught how to behave or how to respect others. When they become teenagers, they just want to do what they want. They do not think about the consequences of their actions. Most of the schools do not teach children how to behave or about morality, just concentrating instead on helping them prepare for their examinations. Somehow, this is not the school's problem. Nowadays, teachers are not allowed to teach many things. They are only allowed to teach from their textbooks and can be in trouble if they talk about certain philosophies or religions. I think most teachers, however, would choose to educate their students to be a good person in society. I am sure that you hear stories from your parent's or grandparent's time. Although they might not have been as highly educated, rich or as successful as some people today, I see that they are more kind and polite. They know how to behave and have more sympathy towards others. This is not like today's generation who think more about themselves and what they want than they do of others.

I do not mean that a martial art teacher should take responsibility for all education. However, I know all good martial art teachers would like to educate their students to behave and to be a kind person as well as having good martial art skill. I am used to saying to my own students, "How you behave reflects back on me and even on my teacher."

A good martial artist firstly has a good nature and heart. They are humble and know how to behave. They respect the skill they have learned, and they also respect their teacher who has given them the skill. You are not born with this skill. Someone has had to spend their time and energy to help you, even your senior classmates have spent time to help you. So do not be arrogant and think you are better than your seniors or even your teacher.

For fighting, you should have good martial art skill and know how to defend yourself if someone wants to hurt you. I know some people who have been studying martial arts for many years. However, when they came to the situation where they needed to defend themselves, they forgot all they had learned and did not know how to use their skill. It seems that they can only be good in a classroom but not in a real situation. I have also noticed that if you have a good nature and are polite, it is rare that someone will want to harm you. Basically you will not draw this kind of attention. This is because you yourself do not try to harm others.

When we study martial arts, we should always try to develop our skill as much as possible. In the beginning, you may only be able to fight one to one and then two or three. At the end, even if someone uses a weapon against you, you can handle it. When you reach an even higher level, you can stop them from hurting you without hurting them. This you can do by controlling your energy. The less energy you use and the better result you get, then this is the best martial artist.

You should not always think about how to do someone the most damage or about seriously hurting your enemy. Always be merciful and give other people an opportunity to turn back, be good and feel remorse for what they have done. Sometimes they do not mean to cause a problem; they are just confused. There are so many movies I have seen where the martial artist breaks someone's arms or legs or even kills them without even thinking or feeling any sadness. That is not a very good martial art attitude. In fact, this is more a western attitude and not one of the traditional martial artist.

On the opposite side, there is Jet Li's film, *Once Upon a Time in China*, where he plays the character Wong Fei Hong, one of China's most famous martial art heroes. In this film, he always tries to stop fighting and to be humble. He only fought when he had no other choice. In the end, there were even some enemies who changed and became good people, all because he tried to help them or saved their lives. You do not see him killing people for fun. It is the same in Bruce Lee's films, he would try to give his enemies the chance to leave and not fight. Jackie Chan's films are the same, and it is rare to even see blood in his movies. This is because in eastern martial arts, we consider more about the heart and moral education.

A good martial artist should also be able to demonstrate his skill, not just watching his students do this for him. A good martial artist should perform in public as well. Many can show their skill in their school, but when they go to the public, they will be nervous or forget the form completely. It does not matter what kind of forms they perform, when someone has good quality, you can see it in their energy. You can see it in the flow of their movement. It is like writing. It should be very clear and you can recognise the words easily. However, no matter how good you are at performing, you should still be humble. Chinese say, "A high mountain, there is always another mountain higher than that."

A good martial artist should also be able to talk fluently about their art, having enough knowledge, philosophy and explanation for all kinds of questions of what they study. When you answer questions, you should be honest about what you study and what you know. You should not lie or pretend. You should be clear about your background and with whom you have studied and who is your teacher. If someone asks something you do not know, then you should say that you do not know and that you will try to find the answer. This is much better than lying and your students will respect you more for this.

A good martial artist should have good fighting skill, cover internal training…this is fist and heart together.

Chinese Superman

How can a bare hand break a brick? How can someone withstand the blow of a sledge hammer breaking a cement slab balanced on their head? How can someone lie on a bed of steel spikes without being punctured or how can they stand being run over by a lorry without being killed? Are these things even possible?

When the Chinese Qigong team came over to demonstrate these amazing skills, many asked, "How can they do that?" or "How can you train like that?". I would say that these people are too innocent. They do not understand how much we can develop the body. Some people in the audience who were more experienced realised that these were Golden Bell, Iron Shirt or high level Shaolin Martial art skills being displayed. These all are real skills which today we call Hard Qigong. Perhaps some of you will ask why we call them Hard Qigong when we are always saying that Qigong is for relaxation. This kind of Qigong is Soft Qigong and is just one side of Qigong practice.

Many books like to classify Qigong into different schools: Daoism, Buddhism, Confucianism as well as medical and martial arts. I prefer to say that there only two schools. One is Daoist and the other Buddhist. Confucian teaching consists of only very simple breathing techniques and many of these have been lost or are no longer practised. Medical Qigong relates to Chinese medicine knowledge and is concerned with the acupuncture points and channels. This is, however, more theory than Qigong practice and so is not a school in its own right.

Finally, there are the martial arts and there are many different kinds, but all are connected with either Buddhism or Daoism because these are the major philosophies and religion in China. These have influenced all of the Chinese martial arts, balancing them and allowing them to develop continually. Confucianism is more narrow and personal and is a way of training your behaviour more than anything else.

The development of Hard Qigong is due to the development of Soft Qigong. In Chinese philosophy, everything must have two opposite poles. Therefore, if we have soft we must have hard to balance. Daoism also follows the principle of Yin and Yang, light and dark, man and woman, etc. Buddhism follows the idea of colours and emptiness. Colours refer to things or objects. The principle follows that everything that you have today, you can see. However, one day these things will no longer be there and so there will be emptiness. The opposite of this is that today you have and see, whereas before, there was nothing. In this way Buddhists tell us not to cherish belongings too much. Buddhists also consider, as does Daoism, the idea of cause and effect. Everything must have a cause to bring it into effect. So every action will also have its own effect or result.

From this we can see that if we have Soft Qigong for relaxation, then we must also have Hard Qigong for fitness and body conditioning. We could even call these exercises Chinese fitness and body building. These methods of training are very different from western methods. In the west people like to train their bodies with weights to make them stronger. However, this way concentrates only on the development of muscles. It can also make you tired because lifting weights is using energy. Chinese fitness training is different as it also considers training for the internal body, not just the external.

Hard Qigong is also external training, but it follows the principles of Yin and Yang. To train the external, you must also develop the internal. Otherwise you may damage yourself. Western weight training concentrates on making the muscles bigger and more defined. Training in this way pushes the blood circulation to the extreme, so afterwards the muscles change shape. It can cause heart problems because of too much stress placed on it. The skin becomes drier because the internal organs by comparison are much weaker and the joints ache because of the stress placed on them. When the external body is too strong, the internal body is weak. These problems occur because we only consider the outside and not the inside.

So how do we train Hard Qigong? First you must train your Dantien, which is the storehouse of all your energy located in the area below your navel. When a singer trains, they must open this area to give more power to their voice. But in Hard Qigong we gather Qi. Qi is air and so in Hard Qigong we need to "eat" the air or swallow the Qi. We do this through special breathing exercises that brings the Qi to the Dantien, thus strengthening and the organs and smoothing the channels.

Hard Qigong concentrates on four main channels: the Ren Channel which runs down the Centre of our front bodies; the Du Channel which runs down the centre of the back; the Chong Channel which runs through the centre of the body itself; and the Belt Channel which runs around our waist. Also, there are two organs which are very important. These are the kidneys which create the internal Qi to keep your mind strong and able to withstand powerful blows. The other is our lungs which enable you to create power for pushing, pulling and hitting.

After a long period of training, your body will become very strong. You will start to train the external body, your muscles, skin and bones. Training involves special ways of carrying heavy objects and even hitting yourself with the bare hands. The blows at first will be light but eventually you will become strong. This exercise we call Pai Da or Kit Pei. Finally you will start to hit the body with special bamboo sticks. The more you practise Hard Qigong, the more energetic and high spirited you will feel. Your body will become stronger and stronger and as you pass through the different levels of training, then eventually you will be able to do the same amazing feats as you have seen performed by other Hard Qigong practitioners.

Hard Qigong is a very strong and healthy exercise, but you need the soft to balance it. Otherwise you will be too hard and too tough. Because Hard Qigong raises the spirit, some may find they have difficulty in sleeping. Others may feel emotionally sensitive or easily get angry. Therefore when we practise Hard Qigong, we must always do meditation. This is a very important part of the training, for without the soft, the hard will finish very quickly. No matter which style of Hard Qigong you study, you should always study with a qualified teacher who can guide you properly. So do not try to study on your own as you could cause more harm to yourself than good.

Two Sides of the Same Face

The martial arts are some of the most attractive skills around. When you go to the movies or watch a video, what an exciting feeling you get as your hero, Bruce Lee, Jackie Chan, Jean Claude Van Damme, Stephen Segal, etc. beats up the bad guys. Having watched the film you might start fighting with your friends—of course, just playing around. But by playing this way you actually release all your emotions and energy. You enjoy this feeling and so maybe you go to find a martial arts class in your area. This might be your story and how you started out studying martial arts.

Some people are very lucky. Straight away they find a good teacher with a lot of skill and knowledge, but others are not so lucky. They follow unqualified teachers, learn incorrect skills and through their training damage their bodies. If you have a good teacher he will teach you morals and principles, how to be good and how to be a gentleman, not just concentrating on fighting. Fighting skill does train your body, but it is not the most important part of martial arts. With good behavior you can control yourself. Otherwise you will be like a buffalo: big and strong but no brain. People who just concentrate on fighting just make their minds more aggressive. This thinking will damage their nature and their health.

As a result of their behaviour, others will not respect them. Automatically they will start looking for reasons to fight and cause problems. If it is just a small problem, they may just break the relationship with their friends, but if it is a big problem then they might end up in prison. Having an unbalanced mentality when learning the martial arts will bring unbalanced results. Good martial artists teach the right attitude. You learn how to respect others, respect your teacher and your seniors. They pass the traditional skills on to you, bring good morals and teach you how to be a good person. Fighting skill is just training.

When you come to learn more about martial skills, you begin to understand more about internal training and external training. Nowadays, many people like to classify different kinds of martial arts, calling dynamic and strong martial arts, "External Martial Arts," like Hung Gar, Choi Lee Fut, Cha Quan, Hwa Quan, Shaolin Fist and even Wing Chun. Actually, styles like Hung Gar and Choi Lee Fut all originate from Shaolin Temple. So people like to call Shaolin Martial Arts "External Martial Arts". Soft and slow styles like Taijiquan, Xing-I, Bagua and Wudang Fist, they like to call "Internal Martial Arts". In fact, we should not call any martial art solely "Internal" or "External". Only different parts of the training can be called internal or external.

Training that concentrates on the bones, muscles and skin is external. Training that concentrates on the Jing, Qi and Shen is internal. However, every martial art should cover both internal and external training. This we call "Wai Gong" and "Nei Gong". Many martial artists only know half of their style and make up the rest and sometimes lie to their students. They like to call themselves "Internal Martial Artists" and put down the "External Martial Arts". In Chinese we say they only have "half a bucket of water" and pretend to know the lot.

Normally such teachers do not belong to any martial family and have betrayed their teachers and made up their own things. Like a frog at the bottom of a well looking up at the sky, which thinks the sky is only as big as the mouth of the well. How much do they know about the size of the sky? Some people who study Taiji, Xingyi and Bagua like to say other martial arts (like the Shaolin styles, for instance) are only external, concentrating on the muscles and physical body with no internal training. They think that these styles are only aggressive. Of course, if you watch Hung Gar, Choi Lee Fut and Shaolin Fist, it is true that they are more dynamic than the slower moving Taijiquan styles or Bagua. But do you really know the meaning of Internal and External martial arts? You should know before you start to classify them.

In 300 BC a Daoist named Zhang Zi said, "I am an outsider traveller". He called himself an "outside person", meaning outside to those people in the secular world. Buddhist monks called themselves "Outside People" and "Outside Family"- "Wai Cha", "Wai" meaning outside and "Cha" meaning family (same as Gar). In China's past, everybody belonged to a village or place. From your surname they could tell where you came from: Chen, Lee, Chaung, Wong, Ho, etc. Each village had its own skill which they called their family skill. It did not have to be a martial skill. It could have been cooking, architecture, carpentry or other skills. So all the monks called themselves Wai Cha and their martial arts were Wai Cha Martial Arts - Outside Family Martial Arts. But many people did not study properly, not read books or ask their seniors about the history. So they created their own stories and then called their skill, Wai Cha Martial Arts or External Martial Arts. They would even try to put down other styles, especially when they themselves knew some internal training.

The Shaolin Temple's martial arts are vey popular, and there is an old saying in China, "All the the martial arts come from the Shaolin Temple". Most other martial styles have in some way been influenced by it. If you name all the martial arts of the Shaolin Temple, they cover so many different ways to train your body, both internal and external. Training starts with your external body concentrating on the bones, muscles and skin, but internally you are also training your breathing, mind and posture. For example, Horse Stance or Sze Ping Ma, has the practitioner stand for a long time, sometimes more than an hour. This is not just training your legs. When you do the Sze Ping Ma your upper body must be relaxed or Yin. Your legs become your root and are strong and so are Yang. So, of course, with a strong root you can develop a powerful body and then concentrate on developing other parts of the body, e.g. head, chest, back, etc. to make them stronger and stronger.

The Shaolin system has many forms: Small Hung Fist, Big Hung Fist, Arhan Fist, Cannon Fist, etc., and many others that are connected with animals like the dragon, crane, panther, snake, tiger, etc. When they are performed they are very strong and powerful, but people watching them might think they are only tough and aggressive. This is wrong! A good master can perform them very comfortably without using too much energy. This is because his movements are also connected with internal training: breathing, mind and posture. With internal training, then in this way, even when you are old, you can still perform the forms very easily and powerfully. This means that your internal body is healthy and strong.

If you are not healthy how can you be fit? All of these forms have a correct way of performing them, otherwise you will damage your body. Shaolin internal training is Qigong, and it covers both Hard and Soft Qigong. Shaolin Martial Arts start with the external body and making you fit, strong and at the same time healthy. Afterwards you learn how to let go of your strength and any stiffness. So at the beginning you start out hard and then you become soft. When that happens your body will be light and you can jump very high, but inside the body will be very powerful!

Shaolin Damo Staff

*"Staff strikes in a whole piece
and the spear hits in a straight line."*

This poem describes the principle of the staff and the spear. The spear and the staff are the kings of the long weapons, although other weapons, like the sword and the broadsword, are more popular. This is because their use is more varied, covering different distances. However, today the staff is a more convenient weapon. Just carrying it to and from class or in your car is easier as few people will look at you. Most will not even notice that you are carrying it all. However, if you were carrying a sword, then the police would definitely look at you and may even stop and ask you why you are carrying a weapon in the street.

Although it is a long weapon, the staff is short in comparison to a pole. However, in Chinese language, a staff and a pole are both called Kwun, regardless of whether it is short or long. They are both the same. A shorter Kwun is sometimes called a Two Headed Kwun

124

because you can use both ends to attack and defend. It is also called an Eyebrow High Kwun because it should be the same height from your feet to the eyebrows. Sometimes they can be a little shorter or longer, though they should not be higher than your head or shorter than your mouth. If it were, it would not be convenient for the way in which it is to be used.

A long Kwun (pole) is usually about seven, eight and even nine feet long. This is a called a Single Head Kwun because you only use one end. You cannot use the other end as it is too long to manoeuvre it. To use a long Kwun you need to use more energy. Sometimes you only use it on one side, left or right, and you cannot change it around as it could be too dangerous. Therefore, the applications of the long pole are different to those of the shorter staff.

For the pole, you need to be very strong and grounded with strong legs. For the staff, you need to be more flexible and lighter. When you are using it you even sometimes need to kick, tumble, jump, using a lot of high and low movements. So the pole is stronger and is more Yang than the staff. The staff is more Yin and lighter. However, all the weapons usually have both Yin and Yang ways of developing.

I have been studying the Damo staff for over ten years with my teacher, Master Wu Chen Yuen. He is a very talented teacher who has a very gentle and humble nature. He is very good at all kinds of Shaolin weapons, from the sword, broadsword, staff, spear, nine-section whip, Spring and Autumn Big Sword, double sword and double broadsword. He is also very good at bare hand forms, and he can still do all of them, even now that he is over seventy years old. He is healthy and flexible and he can do things that many other masters cannot do at his age. One time, he even kneeled down onto the pavement, and then, placing his folded shirt on the ground, he proceeded to a perfect headstand. All of his postures are as close to perfect as I have ever seen.

He practises everyday for at least three hours in the morning. Then he goes home and watches a little television. In the afternoon, he has a nap, visits with friends and then in the evening, he goes out and flies his Chinese kites. Almost everyday he repeats this routine, unless he has something special he needs to do.

You can see many famous masters who reach fifty and sixty years old and they hardly ever practise everyday and then they have health problems. For some of them, their environment does not allow them to do the things they like everyday. For others their exercises are too difficult for them now that they are older. Some are even a little lazy and think they are good enough. They may think that they do not need to practise that much and that they can just enjoy being a master and being respected by other people.

I always think that when a skill is good you should be able to practise it even when you are old, that it should not only be for young people. Today we see a lot of Wushu competitons and the performances are very spectacular. However, they are only for people under the age of thirty or even younger. For anyone older than this, it is very difficult. Older and weaker people cannot do many of the difficult movements because of the tremendous stress it puts on the joints and heavy requirements for flexibility and agility.

The Damo staff is one of my favourite weapons. This is because it can help make your body fit and flexible. After training, your whole body feels light. To practise the Shaolin Damo staff, you need to understand the staff. This is because sometimes you will use the head and other times you will use the bottom of the staff. You also have to know where the centre of the staff is located. This way you can balance the staff when you are rotating it. Otherwise, one side will be longer than the other and feel heavy which can be uncomfortable during training.

For beginners who have never practised the staff before, then it is better to start to play with the staff every day to become familiar with it. You should treat it like a friend. Many people who practise feel awkward. This is because they treat their staff like a stranger. I treat my staff as if it were my friend. I play with it, rotating it one way and then the other, with one hand, with two hands, walking forwards and backwards. Sometimes you can make up your own ways of playing with it and after a while your staff will be like your friend. Then when you use it, you will feel comfortable.

When you begin to practise with the staff, you do not start by learning the form. You first learn how to spin the staff individually. The first exercise is very simple. Standing still, you use two hands to spin the staff clockwise and anti-clockwise. Then you move on to practising by spinning the staff in front and behind you. This is done by starting to spin the staff in front of your body in one hand and then passing it to the other hand and turning round so that it spins behind you. You then turn around again, passing it to the other hand and spinning it in front of you. This is repeated until you can easily spin the staff and turn in a smooth, continuous movement.

After this, you combine this movement with stepping forwards and backwards and changing from on hand to the other. Then, step by step, you can do a whole circle, running and jumping. You will come to like the staff more and more. Once you pick up your staff you will feel very happy. When practising the staff, there are many techinques you can use: hitting, breaking, circling, scooping, sweeping, covering, rotating, pointing, shooting, blocking, spinning and stopping. In all, there are twelve techniques. Different forms have different movements but all are based upon the same techniques.

With the staff, beginners need to understand how to use the body and the staff together. This involves a lot of coordination. To study the staff you do not have to be big or strong. You need to consider flexibilty and coordination more. Each movement relates to energy and posture. Doing the staff will help to correct bad posture particularly with the back and spine. You will find your energy is raised up and your spirit is high.

When you are familiar with the form and can do it without thinking, you should concentrate on the Qi and how to use the energy and the staff together. This is the same for other weapons as well and it makes the weapon come alive.

In China's history, the Shaolin staff is the most famous weapon. You could almost say the staff comes from the Shaolin Temple. In the Tang Dynasty, thirteen monks saved the Tang Emperor when he had been captured by the enemy and thrown in prison. The Shaolin monks fought the enemy army with their staffs, even though the enemy had more powerful weapons. Also during the Ming Dynasty, Shaolin was orded by the Emperor to send monks to fight Japanese pirates who were hijacking Chinese ships and attacking people. Again, Shaolin sent monks armed with staffs to fight.

During the Tang, Song and Ming Dynasties, Shaolin has always had many monks who were trained like an army so that they could protect the country when they were needed.

For the monks, the staff was the most common and useful weapon. However, staff training is not only for self-defence. It is also very good for improving your health, particularly the posture and the balance of the mind.

Wudang Martial Arts

In his book *The Essence of Wudang Martial Arts*, Jin Yee Ming discusses the history of Wudang Martial Arts. He himself was a very famous martial artist who lived in the period of the Republic of China (1912-1949) and is author of several martial art books.

First we must begin with the Shaolin Temple. Remember that the Shaolin Temple dates back to 495 A.D. In the early times, the monks concentrated on Buddhist study and they missed the training of the body. Some monks already knew some martial art skill and started teaching the other monks how to keep healthy. In the beginning they mainly concentrated on physical training and slowly created their own style of internal training and martial arts which was related to the principles of Buddhism. At the beginning, Shaolin

Martial Arts emphasised the hard way and strong physical training. It was later that it became soft and light. This Shaolin system concentrated on breathing and physical training on the bone, muscle and skin. Forward and backward movements are very quick, strong and soft together. "Nei Cha Fist" (Inside Family Martial Art), the Wudang system trains the tendons of the body using subtleness and concentrating on Qigong breathing. Quietness controls action, using the centre of gravity to make the opponent lose his balance.

Like the Shaolin Martial Arts, Wai Cha Martial Arts (Outside Family Martial Arts) have a long history. Wudang Martial Arts are different to Shaolin Martial Arts as they start from the quiet and soft and progress to become strong. With daily practice, these exercises develop the internal power (Qi). When your internal power is strong, your channels will be smooth and your Dantien will be strong. You will approach the level of "Fifty Yang and Fifty Yin" and finally Man and Universe will become one.

Zhang Shan Feng is the developer of Wudang Martial Arts. He was born in 1247 during the Ming Dynasty in Lui Tang Yee district of China. He was interested in Daoism and studied with a Daoist named "Fire Dragon Real Man." Some say that he also studied at the Shaolin Temple when he was young, but these may just be stories about him. He eventually settled on Wudang Mountain to develop his Daoist Alchemy (Daoist Dan and Immortality) for nine years and it was here that he developed the Wudang Martial Arts and Daoist skills for which he is famous.

Zhang Shan Feng wanted to specialise his Wudang Martial Arts and to differentiate them from the Shaolin Martial Arts. So he

called them Nei Cha, (Inside Family) Martial Arts. Nei Cha means people working in someone's family, normally someone who is rich and who has a lot of servants. Those working for them are called Nei Cha Man.

The most popular Wudang Martial Arts are Wudang Taiji, Wudang Bagua Zhang, Wudang Xingyi Quan, Wudang Sword, Thirteen Dragon Spear, Eight Drunken Immortals Quan and Wudang Qigong. These Wudang Martial Arts are based upon the Daoist principles of Yin and Yang, the Five Elements, and Bagua (Eight Trigrams). From slow, they develop to become fast, soft develops to become hard, and the inside develops to the outside. All of these aspects are part of Qigong training following the natural Daoist way.

Most people think that the most popular form of Wudang Martial Arts must be Wudang Taijiquan. Actually, the most popular forms are the Wudang Sword and Wudang Internal training (Qigong). There are still many people who believe that Taijiquan comes from Zhang Shan Feng of Wudang. However, Zhang Shan Feng was a Daoist Alchemist more than a martial artist. He knew martial arts, but probably was not a very high level martial artist. There are many stories about him seeing two animals fighting, like the turtle and crane or crane and snake, which led him to use the same principle of Yin and Yang to create Taijiquan. However, these are just stories, and there is no evidence to prove them.

Wudang Taijiquan is different from the Taijiquan of the Chen, Yang, Wu, Wu(Woo) and Sun families Taijiquan. Fei Xian Wing and Li Chun Shan wrote a book on the Wudang Martial Arts, which covered Wudang Taiji-quan. The poems in this book describe a very different form of Taijiquan from what we practise today, particularly the names of the movements. The names differ a lot, such as "Wild Horse rushes to the Stable", "Black Tiger catches the Heart" and "Wind pushing the Fan" are very different to the poems in the more common styles of Taijiquan.

In the 1950s Xin Cha Jing and Ku Liu Xing published a book called *Chen Family Taijiquan* with evidence to prove that Taijiquan came from Chenjiagou (Chen Village), Henan Province. Chen Wang Ting, alias Zhou Ting, was a knight at the end of the Ming Dynasty and a scholar in the early years of the Qing Dynasty. Chen Wang Ting was known in Shangdong province as a master of martial arts who had defeated more than one thousand bandits. He was the originator of the bare-handed and armed combat boxing of the Chen school. He was a born warrior and was comfortable with both a sword or bare handed fighting.

Chen Wan Ting lived in the middle of the 17th century, when the Ming Dynasty was taken over by the Qing Dynasty. He was the ninth generation of the Chen Family. He passed his skill to five generations, to the fourteenth generation Chen Chan Xing (1771-1853), who taught his family martial art to Yang Lu Chan (1799-1871), who later developed this into Yang Family Taijiquan. Wu Jian Quan (1870-1942) learned from the Yang Family Taijiquan and created his own family style, Wu Family Taijiquan. Wu (Woo) Yu Xing (1812-1880) learned Chen Taijiquan from Yang Lu Chan and also later learned from Chen Qing Ping (1795-1868). He then developed this into the Wu (Woo) Family Taijiquan style. Later, Sun Lu Tang (1861-1932) learned from Wu (Woo) Family Taijiquan and developed his style, Sun Family Taijiquan. These are the five major schools of Taijiquan and they are the most popular in China and throughout the world. There are other styles of Taijiquan but they are still too young in history and are not as popular as those five schools.

Whatever the kind of Taijiquan, they all concentrate on the principle of Taiji -Yin and Yang. The principle of Taiji does not come from Taijiquan, it comes from the Yijing (Book of Changes). The Yijing says that everything comes from nothing: Wuji. Wuji created Taiji. Taiji means Yin and Yang but not being identified, still Heaven and Earth mixed together. Tai means very or extreme. Ji means limit-ation or ending. So Taiji means very extreme and also very limited. When things come to a state of a very extreme or a very limited state, they will split out into two different parts, one of which is Yin and the other is Yang. These we call Lan Yee, which we can divide to form the Four Images— Tze Chang. These can be split to become Eight Trigams—Bagua. This is how the world comes and goes under the principle of the Yijing.

People who study Taijiquan, Xing Yi Quan or Bagua Zhang should follow the principles of the Yijing on which their art is based. Taijiquan has no unique right to the name Taiji and Xing Yee Quan does not own the Five Elements, and Bagua is not a trademark of Bagua Zhang. Therefore, Wudang Taiji can use the same symbol as Chen Wan Ting who created his own Taijiquan. One day you might see someone creating Taiji Kick, or Bagua Claw. Whatever you study, Taijiquan, Bagua Chang or Xing Yi Quan, you should understand the principles of the Yijing, otherwise you are just performing the fighting movements and miss the principle.

"Nei Cha Quan" and "Wai Cha Quan" are both good. Both cover internal and external training: they are equal. Besides those mentioned there are many other styles: Emei Mountain Martial Arts, Qing Xing Martial Arts, Kunlun Mountain Martial Arts, Hon Ton Mountain Martial Arts. Do they belong to Nei Cha Quan or Wai Cha Quan? They are in some ways similar and in some way have their own way. Each martial art has its own style, benefits, and principles. There is no Nei Cha Quan or Wai Cha Quan.

Fist and Heart

When we start to study martial arts, will your teacher teach you how to develop your heart or just teach you how to fight? If not, you might be learning the wrong martial art. You may not learn this in the first lesson, but you should learn this early on. This is a very important part of studying martial arts. A teacher who teaches their students how to fight, should also be responsible for their behaviour. If a student goes out to fight with someone, just because they want to show off themselves or try to make someone scared of them, do you think that this is the kind of person who should learn martial arts?

All the martial artists today watch so many martial art action films where the bad guy is the bully showing off his skill and attacking innocent victims. The good guy always controls his skill until the last moment when he is forced to fight back. Of course, some films just show fighting without heart and this is not a good education for martial artists. When you study martial arts, you can develop very good fighting skill which means you could potentially seriously hurt someone or even kill someone using your bare hands. But is this right? To develop a good heart when studying martial arts is important. A policeman carries a gun and can shoot anyone, but they have rules to govern them. Having a good heart is also about controlling ourselves, particularly children when they begin learning. If they are not educated, they could easily injure other children in playing.

I always find that the most dangerous thing is people who do things unintentionally and therefore cause more serious problems. The first thing in learning martial arts is how to respect the teacher. Chinese people call their teacher "Sifu". Japanese people call their teacher "Sensei". I am sure there are many other names as well in different countries. "Si" means teaching and "Fu" means father. So Sifu means a father for teaching. We can use this same name for both gentlemen and ladies. A teacher should teach their students how to respect the class, how to behave and how to approach others. In the classroom, we should not make fun of other people's movement or say anything that could offend other people. We should not talk back to our teacher when he gives you advice or criticise him if he makes any mistake. We should learn how to be humble to others. When your teacher says something, maybe you find it does not sound quite right. However, you should still respect him because he might have his own reasons. If your teacher did not explain fully, then you should wait until you have the right opportunity to ask, not at a moment when it could embarrass your teacher or other classmates.

To be a good student, you should always consider others not just yourself. So if you say something wrong, do you want other people to embarrass you in front of a group? If not, then you should not do the same to others. Confucius said, "things you do not like or want, then do not offer to others". This makes sense for all kinds of situation. If you can do this, you will not have problems dealing with others. A teacher should be strict for the beginners so that the students can learn how to behave and respect the teacher and skill. Once the student and teacher understand each other, then the teacher does not have to be so strict. This is much better than letting the beginners go along without guidance until they finally make a mistake. I have made this error before. I was not strict for my students in the beginning and it caused me to have to let some of the students go in the end.

We should be humble in every martial art society. Most martial artists consider their style is number one. Actually, if you are the best, you do not need to say this. Not like some masters who say, "I am the best". I can see that the more they say this, the quicker you will not hear of them in the future. If you are good, other people will say so. If you are not good, then they will say so as well.

When we study martial arts, it is easy to come into contact with other styles. It does not matter if you think your style is better than others underneath, you still should be humble and behave and not put down others. Basically, all styles are good if they can give you good health and good fighting skill. Good martial art skill should be able to be practised without causing injury to yourself, no matter what age, even when you are very old.

Many times when we have been studying one style of martial art for a long time, we may want to learn more about another style. This is fine, but you should open your mind and empty your cup of tea before you join in another class. Otherwise you will never learn. There are so many arrogant people who like to say to other styles, "We also do that," or "Oh, we have that technique as well". This is very annoying when a teacher hears someone say this. He may not be interested to hear about your previous experience. Don't forget, you are coming to him, not the other way around. It means you want to learn from him. You should not just give your own comment without thinking or being asked. If necessary, then wait for a good opportunity, for instance, when your teacher asks you, "What do you think of this skill?" Then you can give a comment, but you should still be humble and behave when you answer. This way, you will earn more love and trust from your teacher and fellow students. Otherwise, you cause a problem. Then the teacher does not like you, he may hold back skill from you and you will have lost a good opportunity to learn.

In the future, when you come to a higher level, you will be able to see more clearly both the differences and similarities between styles. A good teacher will always love their students, trying to help them and educate them properly. They will help them to be better martial artists and also a better person. Teachers are also human beings and they will make mistakes. As a student, you should not laugh at them or put them down. This kind of behaviour will not give you credit with others. If a teacher teaches you even one small thing, you should still respect them because that skill has helped you. Do not forget, he is still your teacher. Do not think you are better than your teacher and that you do not need to respect him. This is very bad thinking. A teacher whom you study with, even though he is not the top person in the world, he still has given his knowledge to you in order to help improve your skill and make you better.

A good martial artist does not just have good martial art skill but also should be a good person. Your teacher should show you how to have a good heart and manner, how to help others and respect the seniors and take care of the juniors. If you have a better heart, it will improve your skill and you can reach a higher level. One day you may be a teacher as well. A student wants a good teacher and a good teacher also likes to have a good student.

Teacher & Student

He who does not honour his teacher and who is overly concerned for material things is greatly confused, even though he thinks himself wise.

Lao Zi

Roast Duck

In the Qing Dynasty there lived a very famous martial arts master named Liu De Huan. His skill in martial arts was very high, whether it was barehanded forms or weapons, but he only had forty-six students. This was because he was very strict and would choose his students carefully. Amongst his students was a young man named Jiu Ginzhou. Whenever Jiu Ginzhou went to visit his teacher he would always bring a freshly roasted duck because he knew this was one of his teacher's favourite dishes and that it was not easy to get where his teacher lived.

One day he brought a very fresh roast duck in his village as he was going to see his teacher. On the way it suddenly started to rain very heavily. He had not brought an umbrella with him, so he put the roast duck under his clothes and ran as quickly as he could to his teacher's home. However, his teacher lived quite far from Jiu's village. The weather was still very bad and the rain kept pouring down. When Jiu reached his teacher's house, his clothing was drenched and was wet clear through to his skin.

When Jiu took out the duck from under his shirt, he saw that the duck had changed colour. It had turned from a golden brown to white! The rain had peeled off the skin of the duck and the water had washed all of the taste away. The skin is the best part of a roast duck and is very tasty. Without it, the duck is not very good and does not have any taste. When Jin saw this, he was very upset. Now his teacher would not be able to enjoy the duck.

When he looked up at his teacher, Liu De Huan, he saw his eyes were red as if he were upset and angry. However, his teacher then said, "I have no children. Even if I had some, I do not think they would respect me like you do. If I cannot pass on my skill to you, who can I pass it to?" Finally Jiu became Liu De Huan's best student and inherited all of his skill. Jiu Gin Zhou eventually went on to become the chief of security inside the Qing Palace which today is known as the Forbidden City.

Nowadays many people study with teachers whose skill is very good, but they do not respect the teacher. All they want is the teacher's skill. After they have learned the skill, then they leave and n e v e r contact their

teacher again. It is sad to see the traditional culture has gone. Even in schools today, child-ren do not need to respect their teachers. If they like the subject, they listen and if they do not like it, they do not listen.

The traditional Chinese way is that no matter what kind of skill you learn, whether it is cooking, sewing, Chinese medicine, martial arts or Qigong, the teacher (who we call Sifu, no matter whether they are male or female) and student are very close, like father and son. In the west a lot of students choose their teacher, but good teachers also choose their students as well.

How to Find a Good Teacher

How do you find a good teacher? A lot of this is to do with fate. When you open a magazine, there are many, many advertisements to tell you how good this or that teacher is. Often they will tell you how many days or weeks it will take for you to become a Qigong master or how they will open your Sky-eye (Third-eye). Others may promise that you can learn Qi transmission to heal people. Others promise you secret martial art skill that only they know and many others give themselves titles that they have not earned. Some advertisements look like adverts on TV and some will even say, "Money back guarantee if you are not completely satisfied!" These advertisements do not promote teachers. They only promote commercialism.

A good way to find a teacher is to go and see the person and observe their class. Then you need to ask yourself how you feel about them. You have to look at how they behave and the condition of their health. Whether you want to study Qigong or martial arts, a good teacher will behave well and look very healthy. The teacher should be able to answer your questions so you can understand the skill, just make sure you ask at an appropriate time and politely. No teacher likes to be disturbed when they are teaching others. If they can answer your questions, then their knowledge is clear, and so their skill should also be good.

You should also look at the senior students, people who have been studying for over several years. See how they behave, because if you eventually, study with this teacher, you will most likely become very similar in attitude to these senior students. Learn as much as you can about the lineage of the skill as well. If this is not clear, maybe the teacher has mixed up some things and maybe the result will not be so good.

Recently, I had a student who had studied with me for about one year and then left. Probably she felt she wanted to learn more things more quickly and so she went to another Qigong master. Then suddenly, after another year had gone by, she appeared in my class and asked me how to prevent someone whose energy was very strong from affecting her. I told her that no one could affect you if you do not want to be affected. She replied, "But he is very strong and I cannot get rid of him." So I told her that going to another place might help. However, when I saw her later she looked tired and worried and all her Qi had gone.

From the first, I knew she was too eager to develop her Qi. When she had been studying for only three months, she came to me and said she wanted to teach Wild Goose Qigong. I told her she was not ready. Then, when she had almost finished the form she left. It seems to

me that she just wanted to develop Qi and not the skill or herself. Afterwards she ended up with another teacher, someone who she thought would teach her the power of Qi. She decided to study this skill, but instead of the result she intended, she ended up disturbed.

Studying Qigong should be done step by step. When the time is right, everything will happen. There is a saying, "Three years for small success, ten years to become a living immortal!" It just takes time. Anything that happens quickly can easily result in side effects. You need to be patient. Just practise every day. There is no hurry.

To Behave in Society

We are always looking for ways and ideas to change things for the better. Sometimes, when you find one, you might think it is the right way. However, after some time, maybe after a couple of years, you may find it is not so right after all. For instance, before we had television, everyone was happy listening to the radio. When television was invented we became even happier and when we got colour television everyone went crazy. However, the Chinese say, "When something comes to the end, it bounces back the opposite way."

Today's computerised world is very high-tech. Have you noticed that every few months a new, more advanced model comes out? Technology is getting more and more advanced and so our lives become more easy but faster and faster. You can travel almost wherever you want to go and do whatever you want to do. We can communicate with letters, telephone, mobile phones, pagers and by e-mail. Our minds grow ever more clever, our bodies more comfortable and physically, we do not have to do too much. It is great! We can be lazier and hold back using our bodies so long as we use our brains more.

We do not have to care about our bodies, just make money because whoever makes more money is the more successful person!

Nowadays, in school you do not have to be very well behaved. You can do whatever you like. Some people say it is your right as long as your examination results are high you can get a good job and then make a lot of money. It seems that society's direction for the younger generation, their conduct, behaviour and morality is not so important. As for the teachers in schools, they are restricted in what they can do to make the students behave. As a student, if you do not want to listen or want to misbehave, you can do it because you have your rights.

Some children fail in school so may not be able to get a good job in the future. What will they do? They might have to do anything that they can to make their living. Would you like your children to become like this in the future? What will society be like? When I watch movies from America, it seems that they like to emphasise how badly parents treat their children. Although there are cases like this, they are still a minority and sometimes, discipline is mislabelled and called abuse. I can tell you, when I was young, my father used to physically discipline me and my brothers and sister if we did wrong, but it did not affect our future badly and now we have grown into adults.

More films should tell how parents love their children rather than about children suing their parents. Traditional ways are dying. All parents love their children (only a very few do not). Our ancestors taught us how to educate our offspring and bring them up to be good. Confucius said, "Some children might be strong and some might be weak," but we always say, "A piece of jade needs to be polished otherwise it cannot be beautiful". More and more children are not disciplined and have no control. They need someone to tell them what they are doing wrong and they need guidance and time to mature. Then they will understand morality and how to behave in society. Otherwise, they will make more mistakes when they go on their own. So in schools, how high your marks are is not more important than your conduct, because if you do not know how to behave, how can society be good and kind? If more people knew how to behave, then we would not have so much crime.

Teaching Morality

It is sad to see school teachers going on strike because of a few naughty students. They are very badly behaved, but they are still children, and it is the teachers who are the adults and who have been trained to educate them. However, they are unequipped to change them, so in the end they are forced to go on strike.

This means that the education system has problems. The teachers do not have the strength to educate or punish the children because the children are too protected. Even when they are punished, the punishment is so easy that they are not even afraid of it. Of course, to educate children, you do not have to make students afraid. You have to make them understand their mistakes and the consequences these mistakes can have. You have to make them understand how to be "real people", how to be a gentleman/lady and a person who can be respected. It is not enough to just punish them.

A child has to learn to understand what good is and then they can be useful within society. I am not very good at educating my students. When they come to my class and want to study Qigong or

martial arts, I virtually let them do what they are most comfortable with. After I have taught them, most practise by themselves and I will leave the senior students to help them. I have found this way of teaching has developed a very good atmosphere in the class. However, if someone comes to my class and does not respect other people or the skill I am teaching, I will tell them to leave. I do this because they will affect the other students. Some of my students have been with me for many years and they enjoy the class, improve their health and nature because they become more balanced.

I am not a perfect teacher, and I cannot help everybody. I just want to bring a little morality to those who want to be good and need this way to help them. I do not think it is fair if someone who does not want to study properly starts to disturb other people in the class. I know that there are some people who, when they go to a new class they treat it like their own home. They do whatever they like. For example, maybe they eat, drink or do exercises that they have learned elsewhere from another class. Maybe they take up so much space when they practise that other students are always forced to move out of their way. I find this attitude very selfish and so I have to let them go.

Of course, I usually talk to them first, but if they do not listen I tell them to leave. Normally, however, they leave on their own accord because the class does not have what they are looking for. I find that all my students get on very well, even if they have never met before. When they come together, they are like family and very warm with each other. Teaching skill is an excuse to help people understand morality and what it is to be a real person. This is my aim.

Testing
the
Heart

Once I was talking to a Praying Mantis Kung Fu Master who is from Germany. He is around fifty years old and very easy to talk to. He has a good nature, is very open and will help people as much as he can. He is a good man, who respects his teachers and follows the traditional way of practising. When he was young, he was a sailor and got into a lot of fights in bars. Wherever he went people wanted to fight with him. He did not know why people liked to set themselves on him. He worried that maybe it was because of the way he acted or the way he looked.

Due to his unhealthy lifestyle, he developed serious back problems and he decided he had to do something about it. He was introduced by a friend to a Korean man who taught him some Chen Style Taijiquan. Since then, his back has got much better and he now firmly believes that Chinese martial arts are very good for health. Later, he gave up his job as a sailor to go to Korea to study martial arts. Eventually, he married a beautiful Korean girl and today has a lovely son and daughter.

When he was in Korea, he got a job as a chef in a restaurant and in 1992, he met his Praying Mantis teacher Jiang Kyung-Fang. He told me that his teacher was very strict and told him to always keep the traditional way of training, not to just make the skill look good like in Wushu demonstrations and so lose the real skill. Master Jiang's teacher was Master Hao Honglu. During the Cultural Revolution the Red Guard punished Master Hao. He was made to stand on a table and the Red Guards, who knew his Praying Mantis Martial Arts was good, wanted to test him. They took sticks and beat his legs. Of course, Hao Honglu tried to jump and avoid the sticks. However, the Red Guards shouted, "If your martial art skill is so good, you should be able to stand our hitting." So they made him stand still while they beat his legs. They beat him so long and so hard that eventually he could not stand up. After this, Hao Honglu escaped to Korea. He then passed his skill onto Jiang Kyung Fang, who is my friend's Sifu.

Jiang was a very loyal student. When Hao was very old and in his seventies, Jiang would go to his teacher's home everyday and take care of him. He even went on Chinese New Year which is traditionally a time where people like to enjoy themselves and spend with their families, just like Christmas in the west. He would clean his teacher's house, wash his clothes and even help him to shave and bathe. He helped him with a lot of personal things because he was his teacher and he respected him very much.

The Chinese say, "One day your teacher, whole life your father." Traditionally, in Chinese culture, the teacher was equal to your father.

This is not like it is today where the students treat the teacher like a friend or even as a business partner where they can buy the skill and then sell it to make money themselves later on. Nowadays, there is hardly any real respect of the old ways. Most students only want the teacher's skill. Then, once they have it, the teacher will often never see them again. It is sad to see the traditional culture being lost. How can a good teacher pass on his or her high level skill to students with this kind of attitude? Fortunately, there are still good students who respect their teachers, like my friend, and this makes all teachers who teach the traditional way very happy.

So Jiang Kyung Fang took care of his teacher every single day. Sometimes Hao Honglu shouted at him and scolded him for not doing things right, but Jiang did not mind. He was used to being treated strictly and he knew his teacher was old and his mind was not as clear as it was when he was younger. Jiang looked after his teacher until he died and in the end Hao Honglu taught everything to Jiang Kyung Fang.

My friend told me of an occasion when a arrogant Korean martial artist came to challenge his Sifu. Jiang looked at the way the Korean martial artist behaved and listened to what he said and could not stand it. He accepted the challenge. In less than five seconds, the Korean martial artist was defeated and fell to the ground. Even though he was beaten, he was very impressed by Master Jiang's skill. The next day, the Korean came back to see Jiang, bringing along a box of oranges as a gift. He then asked to be accepted as a student. Jiang was very angry and took the box of oranges and pushed them back to the Korean saying, "I have your oranges. Now you can get out of here." He knew the Korean just wanted to learn his skill just to beat up others and that once he learned, he would leave. He knew this was a bad attitude for the martial arts or indeed any skill.

So the Korean left and never came back. From then on Jiang did not like to teach Korean students, preferring instead to teach Chinese students as they knew how to respect the teacher and skill. In your journey of studying do you find students who do not behave well? These people are like a cancer and can affect even the good students. Although I welcome anyone to be my student, if they do not respect the skill that I am teaching, I think it is better that they find another teacher. I am always sad in this case because unless that person can change their heart, they will never have a good outcome. They will keep changing teachers and never develop a high level of skill. In the end, they may even find themselves become ill or have enemies.

A good teacher loves the skill he is teaching and will love the students who respect this skill.

Further Information

UK

Tse Qigong Centre
PO Box 59
Altrincham WA15 8FS
Tel 0161 929 4485
Fax 0161 929 4489
tse@qimagazine.com

USA

Tse Qigong Centre
PO Box 15807
Honolulu, HI 96830
Tel (808) 528 8501
Fax (928) 441 6578
tse@wildgooseqigong.com

Michael Tse

Michael Tse began his studies of martial arts and Qigong over 25 years ago. He has studied in both Hong Kong and China with some of the worlds most famous teachers, Qigong Grandmaster Yang Meijun lived to 104 years of age, and Grandmaster Ip Chun who is one of the world's leading authorities on Wing Chun Kung Fu. He also studied Shaolin arts with Master Wu Chun Yuen and he is a student of Grandmaster Chen Xiao Wang, the 19th generation inheritor of Chen family Taijiquan.

He has made a name for himself as both a leading authority on the internal arts as well as an international author.

Tse Qigong Centre

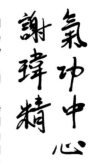

In order to help promote the traditional Chinese skills that he has learned, Michael Tse founded the Tse Qigong Centre in 1990. He now teaches classes and seminars worldwide, helping to promote the skills he has received from his teachers.

The Tse Qigong Centre is growing all the time and now has offices in both the United Kingdom and United States. There is also a growing group of authorised instructors around the world who have been certified to teach the skills of the Tse Qigong Centre. It is his dream to make the skills he has learned more accessible to all and future plans include correspondence courses, futher books and videos.

Master Tse strongly upholds the traditional Chinese values of the student/teacher relationship (like that of father and son) and of respecting the skills that he has been taught. As such, he teaches with heart and morality and he makes all welcome. Those who have studied with the Tse Qigong Centre, often say that it is like an extended family, with many brothers and sisters. It is because of Master Tse's generosity that this family spirit of encouragement and loyality has flourished.

In order to further promote and help others understand Chinese culture, he also publishes Qi Magazine, a quarterly magazine which offers in depth articles on Qigong, Martial Arts, Feng Shui, Chinese medicine and acupuncture, Chinese palm reading and horoscopes as well as philosophy - Buddhism and Daoism.

Those becoming members of the Centre receive a yearly subscription to Qi Magazine, a Centre polo shirt, reduced seminar fees and reduced prices on selected merchandise sold by the Tse Qigong Centre. Anyone is welcome to become a member and may contact the relevant Centre for further information.

Qi Magazine

Qi Magazine was founded by Michael Tse nearly ten years ago as a way of bringing to the West authentic knowledge on Chinese skill and knowledge, such as Qigong and martial arts and Chinese medicine. He has expanded the magazine to include regular articles on Feng Shui, Buddhism, Taoism, Chinese horoscopes and philosophy.

Issue 38

Buddhism Today
Grandmaster Ip Chun &
Wing Chun.
Tai Chi Pracitice
Achieving a natural
Balance.

Issue 40

Grandmaster Yang Meijun
Qigong Healing techniques and
exercises to combat Cancer.
Harmonising your Feng Shui

Issue 46

Grandmaster Wu Chun Yuen
Chinese Sword Skills
TrainingTai Chi in Chen Village
Chinese Palm Reading

Issue 48

Wu Style Tai Chi
Iron Palm Training
Chinese Face Reading
Heavenly Stems & Earthly
Branches of Feng Shui

Qi Magazine now has contributors and readers from around the world and is increasing its distribution regularly to reach a wider audience. It is available by subscription from the Tse Qigong Centre or from your newsagent.

Other Books by Michael Tse

Qigong For Health & Vitality
Companion book for Balancing Gong video. An excellent introduction to Qigong and its benefits. Offers more detailed information about the exercises and meditation.

Wing Chun Traditional Chinese Kung Fu for Self Defence and Health
(co-authored with Grandmaster Ip Chun)
Explore the history of this famous martial art, reputedly created by a woman. Includes stories on Grandmaster Ip Man and his teachers. Step by step photos lead you through simple self defense techniques and the first form, Siu Lim Tao, which is used to develop internal energy and stillness.

Wild Goose Qigong 1st 64 Movements

Wild Goose Qigong is one of the most famous styles of Qigong. Michael Tse is a close student of many years of Grandmaster Yang, the inheritor of this profound skill, and is one of a few who has been authorised to teach her legacy. No other book in the West has been written with such understanding of this subject.

Wild Goose Qigong 2nd 64 Part 1

Filled with more stories of Grandmaster Yang Meijun and some special knowledge never before released. The 2nd 64 helps to rid the body of any prenatal illnesses and problems, but because these kinds of problems are much more difficult to heal, this second set of movements is twice as long as the 1st 64 set and so this book will covers half of the form.

Qigong for Healing & Relaxation

In this full colour book, Michael Tse introduces and explains in great deal the first part of the Healthy Living Gong exercises. He also explains how Qigong can be used for healing many different kinds of illnesses. This fully illustrated book is suitable for people new to Qigong as well as more experienced students.

Qi Journeys Volume II

Another selection of collected stories from Sifu Michael Tse covering many different aspects of Chinese culture, from Qigong, Martial Arts to Feng Shui. There is something for everyone. If you enjoyed Volume I, you will love Volume II.

Video Tapes

Balancing Gong

This video covers all eleven Balancing Gong exercises as from Master Tse's book, Qigong for Health & Vitality. Balancing Gong is a series of gentle movements good for helping improve posture, relieve backache, arthritis, neck injury and knee problems as well as improving balance and coordination. These exercises are suitable for a variety of ages and levels of fitness.

Audio Tape

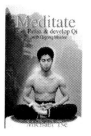

Meditate

In this audio tape, Master Tse introduces you to the concept of meditation and why it is vital to your wellbeing and then guides you through a meditation, helping you to relax and start to feel the benefits of quieting the body and mind.

Visit our website

www.qimagazine.com

For the latest information on seminars, classes and courses.
Also visit the on-line shop for the latest books, videos and magazine